S0-CAH-346

Kagan
Stereochemistry

Volume 3
Determination of Configurations by
Chemical Methods

Stereochemistry
Fundamentals and Methods

Edited by Henri B. Kagan

Georg Thieme Publishers Stuttgart

Volume 3

Determination of Configurations by
Chemical Methods

With Contributions by
J. C. Fiaud, A. Horeau, H. B. Kagan

6 Figures, 53 Tables

Georg Thieme Publishers Stuttgart 1977

6197-5886
SEP./AE

CHEM

Q D
471
F56
CHEM

Editor

Prof. *Henri B. Kagan*

Laboratoire de Synthèse Asymétrique, Bâtiment 420
Université de Paris-Sud
F-91405 Orsay, France

Authors

Dr. *J.C. Fiaud*

Laboratoire de Synthèse Asymétrique, Bâtiment 420
Université de Paris-Sud
F-91405 Orsay, France

Prof. *A. Horeau*

Laboratoire de Chimie Organique des Hormones
Collège de France
Place Marcelin Berthelot
F-75 Paris 5e, France

Prof. *Henri B. Kagan*

Laboratoire de Synthèse Asymétrique, Bâtiment 420
Université de Paris-Sud
F-91405 Orsay, France

CIP-Kurztitelaufnahme der Deutschen Bibliothek

Stereochemistry : fundamentals and methods / ed. by
Henri B. Kagan. – Stuttgart : Thieme.

NE: Kagan, Henri B. [Hrsg.]

Vol. 3. Determination of configurations by chemical
methods / with contributions by J. C. Fiaud ... –
1. Aufl. – 1977.
   ISBN 3-13-132701-4

NE: Fiaud, J. C. [Mitarb.]

Some of the product names, patents and registered designs referred to are in fact registered
trademarks or proprietary names even though specific reference to this fact is not always
made in the text. Therefore, the appearance of a name without designation as proprietary is
not to be construed as a representation by the publisher that it is in the public domain.

All rights, including the rights of publication, distribution and sales, as well as the right to
translation, are reserved. No part of this work covered by the copyrights hereon may be
reproduced or copied in any form or by any means – graphic, electronic or mechanical
including photocopying, recording, taping, or information and retrieval systems – without
permission of the publisher.

© 1977 Georg Thieme Publishers, D-7000 Stuttgart 1, Herdweg 63, Postfach 732 – Composition: Filmsatz Stauffer + Cie., Basle – Printed in Germany by Druckhaus Dörr KG, owner
Adam Götz, D-7140 Ludwigsburg

ISBN 3 13 132701 4

SD
8/9/78
JW

QD471
F56
CHEM

Foreword to the Series

The purpose of this series is to furnish the non-specialist with the fundamentals, principles, methods, and basic references of stereochemistry, the emphasis being on *organic stereochemistry*. The first three volumes are concerned with the determination of absolute and relative configurations or conformations by

(a) IR, NMR, mass spectrometry, X-ray analysis
(b) Dipole moments, CD or ORD
(c) Chemical methods (chemical correlations of configurations, Prelog's method, Horeau's method, asymmetric synthesis and resolution).

Three further volumes are devoted to the following subjects:

(a) Fundamentals of conformational analysis (including calculations by molecular orbital methods)
(b) Stereoisomerism, thermodynamic and kinetic basis of stereochemistry
(c) Fundamentals of dynamic stereochemistry (steric course of reactions, synthesis of chiral molecules).

In two other volumes are described the principles of the physical methods useful for studying stereochemistry:

(a) NMR, IR, Raman, UV, LD, X-ray and neutron diffraction, microwave spectroscopy
(b) Dipole moments, Cotton effect, CD or ORD, chromatography, quasi-racemate method.

The stereospecific methods in organic synthesis will be presented in a separate volume (synthesis of E,Z olefins, asymmetric synthesis, synthesis of diastereoisomers). The discussion will include stereochemically controlled syntheses of natural products or biologically important compounds.

Further volumes on selected topics are planned.

In addition, a Table Volume is available containing additional reference data in an easy to handle form. The objective of the Table Volume is to catalog organic compounds, bearing only one asymmetric carbon atom, the configuration of which has been determined explicitly or implicitly as well as the respective correlation method which has enabled this determination. An encyclopedical review of this type on thousands of optically active substances has not previously been published. It will also be very useful to the preparative organic chemist who starts total synthesis from optically active molecules.

Orsay, spring 1977 *Henri B. Kagan*

Preface

Among the various ways of solving stereochemical problems, physical methods are becoming increasingly important. Nevertheless, chemical transformations still remain a valuable help, especially in the determination of absolute or relative configurations. The term *Chemical Methods* implies the various ways of using *chemical reactions for gaining stereochemical information.*

The first contribution of this volume is a survey of the main chemical transformations which are useful for stereochemical assignments. In some cases, chemical correlations are particularly useful for establishing the configuration of complex molecules. Special emphasis is on the problem of assigning absolute configurations to organic compounds by routine chemical methods. Prelog's method and the partial resolution method (Horeau's method), which are fully reviewed up to 1975, are of special interest for the determination of absolute configurations of chiral alcohols. In many cases, other types of asymmetric syntheses or kinetic resolution are also valuable tools for assigning absolute configurations.

The last contribution presents selected results (including enzymatic techniques) and a discussion of the scope of the methods used.

I thank the authors for their collaboration and H.G. Stahlberg for revising the manuscripts, checking the proofs and compiling the subject index.

Orsay, spring 1977 *Henri B. Kagan*

VIII

Table of Contents

Determination of Stereochemistry by Chemical Correlation Methods

J.C. Fiaud and H.B. Kagan
Laboratoire de Synthèse Asymétrique, Université de Paris-Sud, Orsay, France

Table of Contents

1.   Introduction

Prior to the development of physical methods (NMR, IR, etc.), correlations between stereoisomers were carried out largely by chemical methods and the procedures which were developed are still of considerable utility. The absolute configurations of a great many chiral compounds have been related by chemical means to that of dextrorotatory glyceraldehyde and this approach, i.e. where glyceraldehyde is the ultimate definition point of the chemical correlation, has also been utilized successfully and extensively in natural product chemistry (steroids, terpenes, carbohydrates, etc.).

There are two types of problems which can be solved by the use of chemical correlations, namely
(a) establishment of absolute configuration in a molecule which contains one or more elements of chirality;
(b) establishment of relative configuration (*threo-erythro, cis-trans, syn-anti* diastereoisomerism).
Establishment of absolute configuration in a molecule which contains several elements of chirality obviously necessitates prior knowledge of the relative configuration of the compound. Conversely, the relative stereochemistry of a compound can sometimes be demonstrated by independent determination of the elements of chirality.

Determination of the absolute or relative configuration of elements of asymmetry can be carried out by means of a chemical reaction which either does not modify (direct correlation), or which does modify (indirect correlation), the configuration which is studied. In the latter case, the nature of the modification involved is known. On the other hand, the asymmetry elements in a molecule may be generated by stereoselective reactions such as asymmetric synthesis or asymmetric induction, and the absolute or relative configurations of the elements of asymmetry which have thus been created can often be predicted by analysis of the steric course of the reaction. Stereochemical correlations are most frequently carried out by the direct method, which generally gives reliable and accurate results but which often requires the use of multiple transformations. Correlations based on indirect methods, on the other hand, are rapid and convenient, but the results obtained should be carefully and critically evaluated. The chemist is frequently confronted by two types of problems viz. assignment of an absolute configuration to a chiral substance or demonstration of a relative configuration. As has been emphasized above, these two aspects of a given problem can seldom be treated separately in practice; from the point of view of convenience, however, they are treated separately in the following discussion.

2.   Absolute Configuration

The organic chemist is not fundamentally interested in knowing the absolute configuration of chiral molecules which he uses or prepares. The actual spatial representations of the naturally occurring amino acids, bile acids, etc. are known as a result of curiosity, and Bijvoet's method has been used for such determinations for twenty years. By contrast, it is essential to know the comparative configurations of two chiral compounds where one of the two possible spatial representations has previously been arbitrarily selected for one of the two compounds. The choice of spatial representation which is made constitutes a reference standard with which comparisons may be made. (+)-Glyceraldehyde, the standard chosen by Fischer, was arbitrarily represented by the Fischer projection 1. This choice fortuitously corresponds to the actual situation[1], and the absolute

	CHO				COOH	
H—		—OH		H—		—OH
	CH$_2$OH				CH$_2$OH	

1   **2**

(+)-glyceraldehyde   (+)-glyceric acid

configurations of most of the simple compounds containing an asymmetric carbon atom have been defined with respect to **1** by means of multiple chemical relationships. (+)-Glyceric acid, for example, which is derived from **1** by oxidation of the aldehyde function, necessarily has the absolute configuration **2**. The configurations of certain complex molecules have been very rapidly established by degradation to simple compounds of known absolute configurations. For example, Fischer was able in this way to relate glucosamine to L-serine, which in turn had been correlated with glyceraldehyde. A review of the many chemical demonstrations of absolute configurations in simple molecules is outside the scope of the present chapter, as the results are mainly of historical interest[2, 3] and have been largely collected into tabular form[4]. Instead, the following discussion consists of an appraisal of the reliable procedures which are available for solving stereochemical problems which may be encountered in novel structures. In most cases, a number of illustrative examples are discussed for each method.

2.1. Chemical Transformations which do not Directly affect the Asymmetric Center. Direct Correlation

Relationships based on reactions which do not affect bonds connected directly to the asymmetric center, but which involve bonds remote from it, are unambiguous. Moreover, use of such reactions constitutes a means whereby two compounds may be sterically correlated in the absence of any mechanistic hypothesis (Scheme 1). The literature is replete with determinations based on this principle, and only a single example is given here.

absolute configuration of C(ae, b, c, d)   absolute configuration of C(af, b, c, d).

Scheme 1

Laevorotatory 3,3-dimethylbutane-1,2-diol (**3**) was prepared by enzymatic methods[5] and the absolute configuration established as follows. Monotosylation of the primary alcohol group followed by reduction with lithium aluminum hydride gives 3,3-dimethylbutane-2-ol (**5**) the $S(+)$ configuration of which has previously been determined[6]. Consequently, since neither of the reactions has affected the asymmetric center in **3**, the steric course of the overall transformation is shown by $3 \rightarrow 4 \rightarrow 5$, and it follows that (−)-**3** must have the R-configuration.

R-(−)-**3**   **4**   S-(+)-**5**

[1] J.M. Bijvoet, A.F. Peerdeman, and A.J. van Bommel, Nature **168**, 271 (1951).

[2] J.H. Brewster in A. Weissberger, Techniques of Chemistry, Vol. IV, part 3, p. 1, John Wiley and Sons, New York, 1972.

[3] W. Klyne and P.M. Scopes, Prog. Stereochem. **4**, 97–166 (1969).

[4] J. Jacques in H. Kagan (Ed.), "Stereochemistry, Fundamentals and Methods", Vol. 4: Absolute Configurations of 6000 Selected Compounds with One Asymmetric Carbon Atom (Table Volume). Georg Thieme Verlag, Stuttgart, 1977.

[5] J.P. Guetté and N. Spassky, Bull. Soc. Chim. France **1972**, 4218.

Precautions

Critical examination of the stereochemical scheme of relationship is indispensable, even in those cases where there is certainty that the chemical transformations involved do not directly affect the asymmetric center, the absolute configuration of which is being determined. It is a simple matter to relate a chiral molecule to *one or the other* of the antipodes of a reference substance. Both (–)- and (+)-tartaric acid, for example, have been chemically correlated to the same R(+)-glyceraldehyde[7]; consequently, it is quite obvious that it is not only the net result of the correlation which must be considered, but also the reaction pathway involved. The absolute configurations RR and SS for (+)- and (–)-tartaric acid, respectively, can be deduced by careful examination of routes 1 and 2 (Scheme 2) and without resort to mechanistic hypothesis. As tartaric acid has two identical asymmetric centers with the same configuration, it is necessary to study only one of these centers and to follow the steric course step by step along the whole of the chosen route.

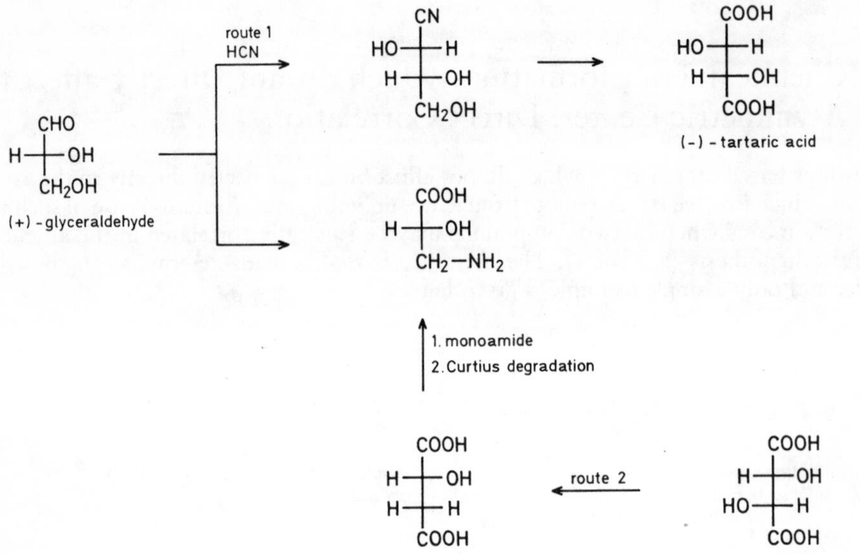

Scheme 2

2.2.   Chemical Transformations involving Asymmetric Centers

2.2.1 With Conservation of the Element of Asymmetry

Many reactions are known in which an enantiomer C(abcd) can be transformed stereoselectively into an enantiomer C(abce). One of the bonds directly attached to the asymmetric center, the C–d bond, is affected in such a conversion, and the question immediately arises as to whether the reaction has proceeded with retention or inversion of configuration. If this question can be answered unambiguously, then the stereochemical relationship between the two compounds will have been established (Scheme 3). Interpretation of correlations based on this principle is considerably facilitated by a knowledge not only of the steric courses of the most important reactions of

[6] J. Jacobus, Z. Majerski, K. Mislow, and P. von Rague Schleyer, J. Amer. Chem. Soc. **91**, 1998 (1969).   [7] D.W. Slocum, D. Sugarman, and S.P. Tucker, J. Chem. Educ. **48**, 597 (1971).

this type but also of the anomalies which may arise either within given groups of related compounds or as a result of the experimental conditions.

Scheme 3

The main reactions used in these correlations are listed in Tables 1–4, and a number of examples are discussed below.

Table 1: Stereochemistry of reactions for the conversion of alcohols into halides or of halides into substitution products[a].

No.	Reaction				Stereochemistry at R^* $R^* = R^1 R^2 R^3 C^*$	Ref.[b]
1	R^*-OH	+	PCl_3	$\longrightarrow$ R^*-Cl	Inversion	8
2	R^*-OH	+	CCl_4	$\xrightarrow{P(C_6H_5)_3}$ R^*-Cl	Retention	9
3	R^*-OH	+	$COCl_2$	$\longrightarrow$ R^*-Cl	Retention	10
4	R^*-OH	+	$SOCl_2$	$\longrightarrow$ R^*-Cl	Predominant retention	11
5	R^*-OH	+	$SOCl_2$	$\xrightarrow{DMF}$ R^*-Cl	Inversion	12
6	R^*-OH	+	$SOCl_2$	$\xrightarrow{pyridine}$ R^*-Cl	Inversion	12
7	R^*-OH	+	$POCl_3$	$\xrightarrow{pyridine}$ R^*-Cl	Inversion	14
8	R^*-OH	+	$Br_2P(C_6H_5)_3$	$\longrightarrow$ R^*-Br	Inversion	15
9	R^*-Br	+	$^\ominus OH$	$\xrightarrow{C_2H_5OH, H_2O}$ R^*-OH	Inversion	16
10	R^*-Cl	+	$R'-CH_2Na$	$\longrightarrow$ R^*-CH_2-R'	Inversion	17
11	R^*-OH	+	$\underset{Cl}{\overset{Cl}{C}}=\underset{N(C_2H_5)_2}{\overset{Cl}{C}}$	$\longrightarrow$ R^*-Cl	Inversion	18
12	R^*-OH	+	PBr_3	$\longrightarrow$ R^*-Br	Inversion	

[a] See p. 9 for the anomalies that can arise as a result of intramolecular participation by a functional group.
[b] See Ref.[19, 20] for detailed discussions of substitution reactions.

[8] J. Kenyon, A.G. Lipscomb, and H. Phillips, J. Chem. Soc. **1931**, 2275; E.J. Coulson, W. Gerrard, and H.R. Hudson, J. Chem. Soc. **1965**, 2364; J.B. Lee and T.J. Nolan, Tetrahedron **23**, 2789 (1967).

[9] R. Aneja, A.P. Davies and J.A. Knaggs, Tetrahedron Lett. **1974**, 67.
[10] M.B. Harford, J. Kenyon and H. Phillips, J. Chem. Soc. **1933**, 179; K.B. Wiberg and T.M. Shryne, J. Amer. Chem. Soc. **77**, 2774 (1955).

Table 2: Stereochemistry of rearrangement reactions which affect an asymmetric center.

Reaction	Stereochemistry at R^* $R^* = R^1 R^2 R^3 C^*$	Ref.
Nitrous acid deamination: $R^* - NH_2 \longrightarrow R^* - OH$	Predominant retention[a]	[21]
Hofmann rearrangement: $R^* - CO - NH_2 \longrightarrow R^* - NH_2$	Retention	[22]
Curtius rearrangement: $R^* - CO - N_3 \longrightarrow R^* - NH_2$	Retention	[23]
Schmidt rearrangement: $R^* - COOH \longrightarrow R^* - NH_2$	Retention	[24]
Lossen rearrangement: $R^* - CO - NHOH \longrightarrow R^* - NH_2$	Retention	[25]
Baeyer-Villiger oxidation: $R^* - CO - R' \longrightarrow R^* - O - CO - R'$	Retention	[26]
Wolff rearrangement; Arndt-Eistert reaction $R^* - COOH \longrightarrow R^* - CO - CHN_2 \longrightarrow R^* - CH_2 - COOH$	Retention	[27]
Stevens rearrangement: $R^* - \overset{\oplus}{\underset{R}{N}} - CH_2 - R \overset{B^{\ominus}}{\longrightarrow} R^* - \underset{R}{\underset{\mid}{CH}} - N \big\langle$	Partial retention	[28, 29]
Wittig rearrangement: $R^* - O - CH_2 - R' \overset{B^{\ominus}}{\longrightarrow} R^* - \underset{OH}{\underset{\mid}{CH}} - R'$	Partial retention	[29, 30, 31]
Amino alcohol deaminations:	Inversion	[32]
	Retention at R^*	[33]

[a] With amino acids and *equatorial* alicyclic amines; with aliphatic amines and amino esters inversion is accompanied by racemization.

[11] J. Kenyon, H. Phillips and F.M.H. Taylor, J. Chem. Soc. **1931**, 382; P.D. Bartlett and H.F. Herbrandson, J. Amer. Chem. Soc. 74, 5971 (1952); E.S. Lewis and C.E. Boozer, J. Amer. Chem. Soc. 75, 3182 (1953); D.J. Cram, J. Amer. Chem. Soc. 75, 332 (1953).

[12] M. Ikehara, H. Uno, and F. Ishikawa, Chem. Pharm. Bull. (Tokyo) 12, 267 (1969).

[13] E.S. Lewis and C.E. Boozer, J. Amer. Chem. Soc. 74, 308 (1952).

[14] R.L. Burwell, A.D. Shields, and H. Hart, J. Amer. Chem. Soc. 76, 908 (1954).

[15] J.P. Schaeffer and D.S. Weinberg, J. Org. Chem. 30, 2635, 2639 (1965).

[16] E.D. Hughes, C.K. Ingold, and S. Masterman, J. Chem. Soc. **1937**, 1196, 1236.

[17] A.J. Speziale and R.C. Freeman, J. Amer. Chem. Soc. 82, 903, 909 (1961).

[18] A. Streitweiser Jr., J. Amer. Chem. Soc. 75, 5014 (1953); P.J. Skell, J. Amer. Chem. Soc. 82, 410 (1960).

[19] C.K. Ingold, "Structure and Mechanism in Organic Chemistry", 2nd Edit., p. 509, Cornell University Press, 1969.

[20] E.S. Gould, "Mechanism and Structure in Organic Chemistry", p. 263, Holt and Co, N.Y., 1959.

[21] P. Brewster, F. Hiron, E.D. Hughes, C.K. Ingold, and P.A.D. Rao Nature 166, 179 (1950); K. Koga, M. Taniguchi, and S. Yamada, Tetrahedron Lett. **1971**, 263.

[22] C.L. Arcus and J. Kenyon, J. Chem. Soc. **1939**, 916.

Table 3: Stereochemistry of the substitution reactions at asymmetric carbon, sulfur, and silicon which are commonly used in chemical correlations of configuration.

Substrate	Reagent	Product	Stereochemistry	Ref.
$R^*-B\diagdown^{\diagup}$	$H_3C-COOD$	R^*-D	Retention	[34]
	$H_2O_2/NaOH$	R^*-OH	Retention	[35]
	$H_2N-O-SO_3H$	R^*-NH_2	Retention	[36]
	$CO/LiAlH(OCH_3)_3$	R^*-CHO	Retention	[37]
	$Br-CH_2-COOC_2H_5$ / $(H_3C)_3C-OK$	$R^*-CH_2-COOC_2H_5$	Retention	[37]
	$H_2C=CH-CHO/H_2O$	$R^*-(CH_2)_2-CHO$	Retention	[37]
$\underset{R^1}{\overset{H}{\diagup}}C=C\underset{R^2}{\overset{B-}{\diagdown}}$	$H_3C-COOH$	$\underset{R^1}{\overset{H}{\diagup}}C=C\underset{R^2}{\overset{H}{\diagdown}}$	Retention	[38]
$R^1-\overset{*}{\underset{\downarrow O}{S}}-OR^2$	R^3-MgX	$R^1-\overset{*}{\underset{\downarrow O}{S}}-R^3$	Inversion	[39]
$\overset{*}{Si}\rightarrow O$	HY^a/Pd	Si^*-Y^a	Inversion	[40]
	Cl_2	Si^*-Cl	Retention	[41]
	$H_2C=CH-R/Pt/H_2$	$Si^*-(CH_2)_2-R$	Retention	[42]
Si^*-Cl	$R-M^b$	Si^*-R	Inversion	[43]
Si^*-H	$R-M^b$	Si^*-R	Predominant retention	[43]

$R^* = R^1R^2R^3C^*$, $Si^* = R^1R^2R^3Si^*$
[a] $Y = OH, OR, O-CO-R, OAr, NR_2, NH-R$
[b] $M = MgBr, Li$

[23] J. Kenyon and D.P. Young, J. Chem. Soc. **1941**, 263; P.A.S. Smith, Org. React. **3**, 337 (1946).

[24] J. Berson and D.A. Ben Efraim, J. Amer. Chem. Soc. **81**, 4094 (1959); H. Wolff, Org. React. **3**, 307, 1946.

[25] A. Campbell and J. Kenyon, J. Chem. Soc. **1946**, 25; E.S. Wallis and R.D. Dripps, J. Amer. Chem. Soc. **55**, 1701 (1933); E.S. Wallis and S.C. Nagel, J. Amer. Chem. Soc. **53**, 2787 (1931).

[26] K. Mislow and J. Brenner, J. Amer. Chem. Soc. **75**, 2318 (1953); D.J. Cram and J. Allinger, J. Amer. Chem. Soc. **76**, 4516 (1954).

[27] K.B. Wiberg and T.W. Hutton, J. Amer. Chem. Soc. **78**, 1640 (1956); W.E. Bachmann and W.S. Truve, Org. React. **1**, 38, 1942.

[28] J.H. Brewster and M.W. Kline, J. Amer. Chem. Soc. **74**, 5179 (1952).

[29] S.M. Pine, J. Chem. Educ. **48**, 99 (1971).

[30] V. Schollkopf, Angew. Chem. Int. Edit. **2**, 161 (1963).

[31] V. Schollkopf and D. Walter, Justus Liebigs Ann. Chem. **654**, 27 (1962).

[32] B.M. Benjamin, H.J. Schaeffer and C.J. Collins, J. Amer. Chem. Soc. **79**, 6160 (1957).

[33] R.A. Moss, Chem. Eng. News **1971**, 28.

[34] H.C. Brown and K.J. Murray, J. Org. Chem. **26**, 631 (1961).

[35] H.C. Brown and G. Zweifel, J. Amer. Chem. Soc. **83**, 7544 (1961).

[36] M.W. Rathke, N. Inoue, K.R. Verma, and H.C. Brown, J. Amer. Chem. Soc. **88**, 2870 (1966).

[37] H.C. Brown, M.M. Rogic, M.W. Rathke, and G.W. Kabalka, J. Amer. Chem. Soc. **91**, 2150 (1969).

[38] H.C. Brown and G. Zweifel, J. Amer. Chem. Soc. **83**, 3834 (1961).

Table 4: Stereochemistry of addition reactions to $R^1 R^2 R^3 P^{*a}$.

Reagent	Product	Stereochemistry of the product at P^*	Ref.
X_2	$R^1 R^2 R^3 PX_2$	Inversion	[45]
H_2O_2	$R^1 R^2 R^3 P \rightarrow O$	Retention	[46]
R^4-X	$R^1 R^2 R^3 P^{\oplus} X^{\ominus}$	Retention	[47]
S, episulfides	$R^1 R^2 R^3 P = S$	Retention	[48]
$Ar-N_3$	$R^1 R^2 R^3 P = N-Ar$	Retention	[49]
RLi ($R^3 = CH_3$)	$R^1 R^2 P - CH_2Li$	Retention	[50]

a for a review, see Ref.[44]

Methods based on substitution reactions are potential sources of multiple correlations, but the results obtained must be analyzed very carefully with respect to experimental conditions. Thus, Walden showed at the end of the 19th century that substitution may proceed with either retention or inversion[51] (Scheme 3).

Scheme 3.

Conversion of an alcohol into the corresponding halide derivative is a classic stereochemical problem as, indeed, are analogous substitution processes, notably the reactions of alkyl halides with a variety of nucleophiles. It is difficult to generalize the situation in these transformations with respect to stereochemistry when the hydroxy or another leaving group (halogen, tosyl) is directly attached to the asymmetric center. Thus, methods are known in which the conversion $R^*-OH \rightarrow R^*-Cl$ or R^*-Br may be accompanied by either inversion or retention of configuration.

Nucleophilic substitution reactions $R-X \rightarrow R-N$ normally proceed with inversion if the mechanism is S_N2, but are accompanied by racemization if the mechanism is S_N1.

[39] M.M. Green, M. Axelrod and K. Mislow, J. Amer. Chem. Soc. 88, 861 (1966); D.J. Sandman, K. Mislow, W.P. Giddings, J. Dirlam, and G.C. Hanson, J. Amer. Chem. Soc. 90, 4877 (1968).

[40] L.H. Sommer and J.E. Lyons, J. Amer. Chem. Soc. 91, 7061 (1969).

[41] R. Corriu and G. Royo, Tetrahedron 27, 4289 (1971).

[42] L.H. Sommer, J.E. Lyons and H. Fujimoto, J. Amer. Chem. Soc. 91, 7051 (1969).

[43] L.H. Sommer, W.D. Korte, and P.G. Rodewald, 89, 862 (1967); L.H. Sommer and W.D. Korte, J. Amer. Chem. Soc. 89, 5802 (1967); R. Corriu and G. Royo, Bull. Soc. Chim. France 1972, 1497.

[44] M.J. Gallagher and I.D. Jenkins, Top. Stereochem. 3, 1 (1968).

[45] L. Horner and H. Winkler, Tetrahedron Lett. 1964, 455.

[46] L. Horner, Pure Appl. Chem. 9, 225 (1964); O. Cervinka and O. Kriz, Collect. Czech. Chem. Commun. 31, 1910 (1966).

[47] L. Horner, H. Fuchs, H. Winkler, and A. Rapp, Tetrahedron Lett. 1963, 965.

[48] D.P. Young, W.E. McEwen, D.C. Velez, J.W. Johnson, and C.A. Vanderwerf, Tetrahedron Lett. 1964, 359.

[49] L. Horner and H. Winkler, Tetrahedron Lett. 1964, 175.

[50] L. Horner, W.D. Balzer and D.J. Peterson, Tetrahedron Lett. 1966, 3315.

[51] P. Walden, Ber. 29, 133 (1896); 30, 3146 (1897).

Various methods for the preparation of halogen derivatives, starting from an alcohol in which the hydroxy group is directly attached to an asymmetric carbon atom, are listed in Table 1. The reverse transformation is also indicated together with its stereochemistry, as well as several other nucleophilic substitution processes which are useful in stereochemical correlations. A number of rearrangement reactions which can be used for the transformation of a carboxy group into an amino, methoxycarbonyl, or bromine group, or for isomerization of amines and ethers, are given in Table 2.

Example:
Consider the problem of relating the acid $R^1R^2R^3C^*-COOH$ stereochemically to the alcohol $R^1R^2R^3C^*-OH$: method number 6 in Table 2 (Baeyer-Villiger oxidation) on the corresponding methyl ketone would provide the answer. Alternative procedures are also obviously possible, but they are less direct, e.g. reaction number 4 followed by reaction number 1 of Table 2.

Precautions which should be observed in the utilization of the methods given in Table 1.
There are exceptions to the stereochemical rules indicated in Table 1 and these have been observed in cases where there is a functional group in the vicinity of the reaction center which can participate in a nucleophilic substitution reaction. Treatment of ethyl 2-bromopropanoate with dilute sodium hydroxide, for example, gives ethyl lactate with inversion of configuration, while conversion of the sodium salt of 2-bromopropanoic acid into lactic acid under the same conditions proceeds with retention of configuration. In the latter case the carboxylate ion displaces the bromine intramolecularly and the reaction results in inversion. The intermediate α-lactone then undergoes ring opening to give lactic acid by attack of hydroxide ion, and this reaction also proceeds with inversion. The overall result of this double inversion process is obviously retention

direct substitution   neighboring group participation

of configuration[52]. Heteroatoms (halogens, ether and ester oxygen[53], double bonds[54], and aromatic nuclei[55]) are included in neighboring groups which are nucleophilic and which can participate in such reactions.

2.2.2. Intramolecular Transfer of Chirality

This particular aspect is concerned with the transformation of one substance which contains an element of chirality into a compound which contains another element of chirality. Included within this area are substitution, elimination and rearrangement reactions whereby a substrate is converted into a chiral product; these processes have been reviewed[56, 57].

2.2.2.1. A Transfer of an Asymmetric Center

[52] W.A. Cowdrey, E.D. Hughes and C.K. Ingold, J. Chem. Soc. **1937**, 1208; **1938**, 1243; S. Winstein and H.J. Lucas, J. Amer. Chem. Soc. **61**, 1576 (1939).

[53] S. Winstein, J. Amer. Chem. Soc. **64**, 2780, 2787 (1942); **65**, 613 (1943); S. Winstein, E. Allred, R. Heck, and R. Glick, Tetrahedron 3, 1 (1958).

1,3-Transfer of the benzylic proton in **6** gives **7** and the reaction is highly stereoselective. The mechanism very probably involves transfer of the proton across one face of the indene ring by means of "tight" ion pairs. The configuration of **7** can therefore be deduced from that of **6**[58]. Conversion of the vinyl ether **8** into the aldehyde **9** proceeds analogously, i.e. formation of the

C–C bond and cleavage of the C–O bond occur on the same face of the cyclic system (suprafacial reaction)[59].

The stereochemistry of the products obtained from rearrangements of this type (sigmatropic reactions) can be predicted in many cases by use of the Woodward-Hoffmann rules[60].

2.2.2.2. The Substrate has Central Chirality and the Product Axial or Molecular Chirality

The configurations of the allenes **11** obtained by rearrangement of certain precursors which have central chirality can be established by consideration of the stereochemistry of the rearrangement process and the configurations of the precursors[61]. Conversion of **10** into **11**, for example, probably proceeds via a cyclic, intramolecular $S_N i$ mechanism.

The decomposition of optically active N-nitroso-N-cyclopropylcarbamates **13**, which are prepared from the cyclopropanecarboxylic acids **12**, also gives chiral allenes[62]. Ring opening of the intermediate diazacyclopropanes is probably a conrotatory process (disrotation would lead to *racemic* allenes) and the direction of rotation of the bonds is that in which the R/R interactions

$R = CH_3, C_2H_5, C_4H_9, C_6H_5$

[54] C.W. Shoppee, J. Chem. Soc. **1946**, 1147; S. Winstein, M. Shatarsky, C. Norton, R.B. Woodward, J. Amer. Chem. Soc. 77, 4183 (1955); J.B. Rogan, J. Org. Chem. 27, 3910 (1962); R.G. Lawton, J. Amer. Chem. Soc. 83, 2399 (1961).

[55] D.J. Cram, J. Amer. Chem. Soc. 71, 3863 (1949).

[56] J. Morrison and H.S. Mosher, Asymmetric Organic Reactions, p. 374, Prentice Hall, Englewood Cliffs, New York, 1971.

[57] G. Krow, Top. Stereochem. 5, 31 (1970).

[58] J. Almy, R.T. Uyeda, and D.J. Cram, J. Amer. Chem. Soc. 89, 6768 (1967); 91, 4459 (1969).

[59] R.K. Hill and A.G. Edwards, Tetrahedron Lett. 1964, 3239.

[60] N'Guyen Trong Anh, Les règles de Woodward-Hoffmann, p. 45, Ediscience, Paris, 1970.

[61] R. Rossi and P. Diversi, Synthesis 1973, 25.

[62] J.M. Walbrick, J.W. Wilson Jr., and W.M. Jones, J. Amer. Chem. Soc. 90, 2895 (1968).

are minimized. Consequently, the expected result is the formation of an excess of the enantiomer 14. This reaction sequence offers a method for the determination of the configuration of 14, or at the least for the correlation with the configurations of the acids 12 which are not known in all of the cases cited[63].

2.2.2.3. The Substrate has Axial Chirality and the Product Central Chirality

The configurations of allenes have been correlated in many cases with those of compounds having central chirality. Thus, oxymercuration, bromination and iodination of allenes give *trans*-addition products; the reactions are highly stereoselective[64]. It is therefore predictable that bromination of R(–)-dimethylallene 15 in ether will give the *trans*-compound 16 as the preponderant isomer.

2.2.3. Asymmetric Synthesis

An optically active compound can be prepared from a prochiral substrate by asymmetric synthesis, which involves the use of a chiral reagent, catalyst or solvent; in a large number of cases it has been possible to predict the absolute configuration of the product by examination of the steric course of the reaction. Applications of asymmetric syntheses and kinetic resolution to the determination of configuration will be discussed on p. 94.

3. Determination of Relative Configurations

It is useful to know how to determine the relative configurations of the asymmetric centers in a given molecule, and in particular in a natural product. It is thus important to know the α or β orientation of a substituent group at a given position in a steroid, in a carbohydrate, in an alkaloid. If the relative configurations of all of the chiral elements in a molecule and if also the absolute configuration of one of them are known, then the absolute configurations of all of the elements of chirality can be deduced.

Example:
Cholic acid is a natural product which contains eleven asymmetric centers, and hence there are 2^{11} (2048) stereoisomers or 1024 pairs of enantiomers. The relative configurations of these eleven asymmetric centers are known as a result of X-ray diffraction studies, and determination of the absolute configuration at C-3 has enabled the absolute configurations of the remaining ten asymmetric centers to be deduced.
Determination of the relative configurations of two centers is important, as it facilitates prediction of their absolute configurations. In principle, spectroscopic analytical techniques such as NMR and IR can be used for the determination of relative configurations. In practice, however, chemical methods, which involve the use of reactions of known or postulated stereochemistry, are still valuable. Most of the known stereoselective reactions have been used in such stereochemical studies, and it follows that the most useful reactions are those in which the stereoselectivity is highest and best understood.

---

[63] W.L. Waters, W.S. Linn, and M. Caserio, J. Amer. Chem. Soc. 90, 6741 (1968).

[64] W.M. Jones, J.W. Wilson, Jr., and F.B. Tutweiler, J. Amer. Chem. Soc. 85, 3309 (1963).

By analogy with the previously discussed treatment of the determination of an absolute configuration, procedures for the determination of relative configurations are divided into four categories:

3.1.   Reactions which do not affect Relative Configurations

The relative configuration *(cis-trans, threo-erythro)* of a compound can be revealed by means of a reaction which involves two of the substituent groups which participate in the establishment of the stereochemistry. The ease with which the reaction proceeds depends on the relative positions of these two groups in each of the diastereoisomers and provides information on the stereochemistry of the compound.

In cyclic compounds, for instance, the geometric constraints imposed by the ring system are such that often only one epimer of a pair of diastereoisomers will participate in an intramolecular reaction. It is therefore sometimes possible, by examination of the respective reactivities of the two epimers, to deduce the stereochemistry at the centers carrying the reacting groups. For example, determination of the relative configurations of cyclic *vicinal* diols is facilitated by the observation of the ease with which they form borate esters, carbonate esters or acetals[65]. Thus, *meso*-butane-2,3-diol complexes with boric acid more readily than the (±)-isomer; in the former case the methyl-methyl interactions in the complex are *trans,* whereas in the latter they are *gauche.* Similarly, *cis*-cyclohexane-1,2-diol readily forms an isopropylidene derivative while the *trans* isomer does not. Finally, *cis*-1,2-diols are generally oxidized more rapidly by periodate or permanganate than the trans isomers as the formation of a cyclic intermediate is more favored in the *cis*-isomer.

Similar considerations may also be applied to the establishment of the *cis-trans (Z,E)* configuration of olefinic compounds. Thus, the A and X groups in 17 react more readily than those in 18 to give as only the former can produce or cyclic intermediate. Maleic acid, for example, in which the

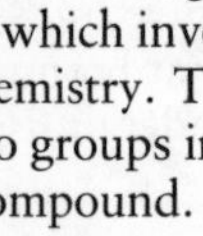

17 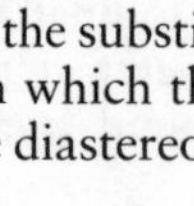   18

carboxy groups are *cis,* readily forms an anhydride while fumaric acid, in which the carboxy groups are *trans,* does not. Similarly, the *cis*-cinnamic acids 19 undergo facile cyclization to indenones. The ease with which hydroxy acids undergo lactonization depends on the relative

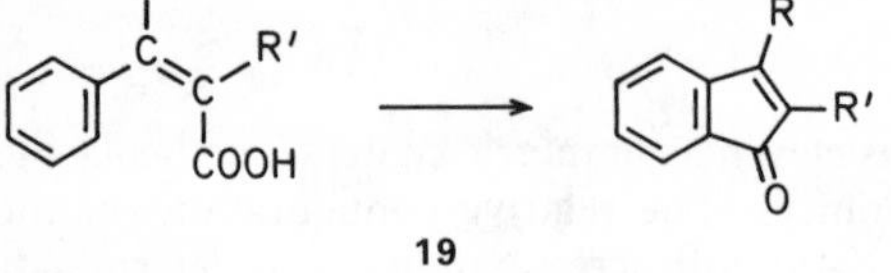

19

dispositions of the hydroxy and carboxy groups; thus, *cis*-4-hydroxycyclohexanecarboxylic acid, can lactonize, whereas the *trans*-isomer cannot.

3.2.   Reactions involving one of the Elements which define the Relative Configuration

3.2.1.   Without Change in the Nature of the Diastereoisomerism

The reactions, comments and precautions given in 2.2. are valid for compounds which show *threo-erythro*-diastereoisomerism. Stereospecific reactions at vinylic positions are also possible[66] and have been used both in synthesis and in chemical correlations. Substitution of a vinyl bromine by an alkyl group by the use of lithium dialkylcuprates, for example, is known to proceed with retention of configuration[67].

3.2.2.   Interconversion of Types of Diastereoisomers

Procedures are known for the transformation of geometric isomerism into *threo-erythro* diastereoisomerism and vice versa.

3.2.2.1. Conversion of *E,Z*-Diastereoisomers into *threo-erythro* Diastereoisomers

This section is concerned with the addition of compounds a–b to olefinic substrates. Addition of the elements a and b of the reagent a–b to an olefin 20 can give either diastereoisomers A or B

depending on the orientation of addition (a–b or b–a). From a knowledge of the stereochemistry of addition (*syn* or *anti*) it should be possible to establish a correlation between the *E* or *Z* configuration[68] of the olefin and the relative *threo* or *erythro* configuration of the addition product 21 or 22. Moreover, if the reaction is carried out with a chiral olefin, then addition will preferentially occur on the least sterically hindered side of the double bond. Consequently, a choice can be made between 21 A and 22 A and their enantiomers.

The stereochemistry of catalytic hydrogenation of olefins has been well reviewed and discussed[69, 70] as has the stereochemistry of electrophilic addition of acids, peracids, halogens and sulfenyl halides to olefins[71]. Most of the synthetic procedures which involve formation of a cyclic intermediate of the type 23 proceed via *syn* addition and the configuration of the starting olefin is retained in the product, as for example in the formation of epoxides, the preparation of diols by *syn*-hydroxylation with osmium tetroxide, and the addition of carbenes or carbenoids to olefins. The stereochemistry of these additions has been reviewed[72].

[65] R. J. Ferrier, Progr. Stereochem. 4, 85 (1969).
[66] J.H. Brewster, in A. Weissberger, Techniques of Chemistry, Vol. IV, part 3, p. 24, John Wiley and Sons, New York, 1972.
[67] H.O. House, W.L. Respess, and G.M. Whitesides, J. Org. Chem. 31, 3128 (1966).
[68] J.E. Balckwood, C.L. Gladys, K.L. Loening, A.E. Petratca, and J.E. Rush, J. Amer. Chem. Soc. 90, 509 (1968).

[69] R.L. Burwell Jr., Chem. Rev. 57, 895 (1957).
[70] S. Siegel, Advan. Catal. 16, 124 (1966).
[71] J.H. Brewster, in A. Weissberger, Techniques of Chemistry, Vol. IV, part 3, p. 93, John Wiley and Sons, New York, 1972.
[72] G.L. Closs, Top. Stereochem. 3, 193 (1968).
[73] N'Guyen Trong Anh, Les règles de Woodward Hoffmann, p. 16, Ediscience, Paris, 1970.

The relative stereochemistry of products obtained from electrocyclic reactions can be predicted by means of the Woodward-Hoffmann rules[73]. Thus, 2,4,6-octatriene **24** can cyclize to either *cis* or *trans*-5,6-dimethylcyclohexa-1,3-diene **25** depending on the reaction conditions. Such predictions are equally valid for concerted cycloaddition reactions, a particular case of which is the Diels-Alder reaction. Here, the stereochemistry is supra-supra, and hence the *endo*-adduct is obtained. Moreover the relative configuration of the product formed in a Diels-Alder reaction can be exactly predicted as the following rules[74] are observed:

(i) the diene reacts in a suprafacial manner in the *s-cis* configuration and this arrangement is conserved in the double bond of the product;

(ii) the configuration of the dienophile is also conserved in the product.

Even so, steric and dipole effects in the transition state should always be considered.

By use of these rules, the *trans*-configuration can be assigned to the product obtained from the reaction of butadiene with *trans*-1,3-diphenyl-propenone **26**.

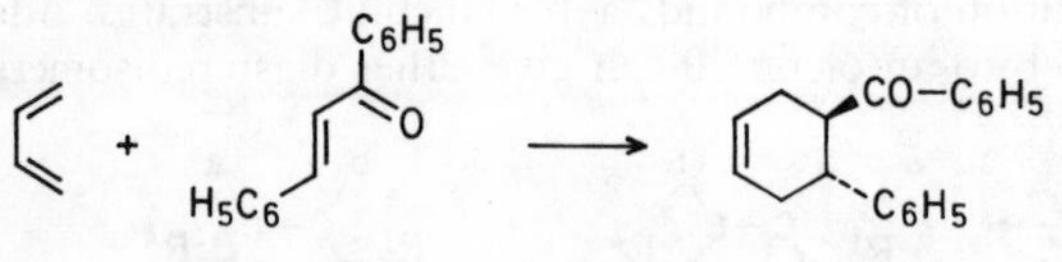

Under the conditions of kinetic control, the addition of diborane and organo-boranes to olefins occurs in a *syn* fashion and the reactions are very stereoselective; the boron moiety adds to the less substituted carbon atom in a highly stereospecific manner and with retention of configuration (see Table 3, p. 7).

3.2.2.2. Conversion of *threo-erythro* Diastereoisomers into *E,Z*-Diastereoisomers

This section is devoted to all reactions which involve conversion of *threo-erythro* compounds to into olefins, and in particular elimination reactions. Of the many known types of elimination reactions dehydration, dehydrohalogenation and detosylation do not follow a predictable steric course. On the other hand, if a reaction proceeds by a synchronous cyclic transition state and the structure of the olefinic product is known, then the relative configuration of the starting material can be predicted with a high degree of accuracy (and vice versa). Examples of the latter type of process are the pyrolysis of dithiocarbonate O-esters[75] and of tertiary amine oxides[76] and the elimination of phosphine oxides from betaines[77].

Procedures for the stereospecific and stereoselective synthesis of olefins have been reviewed and discussed[78–80]. Here again, the configurations of the olefinic products obtained from concerted electrocyclic reactions and sigmatropic reactions can be predicted by use of the Woodward-Hoffmann rules[81]. Decomposition of the cyclopropyldiazonium ions **27** and **28**, for example, exclusively leads to the formation of the *trans*-cinnamyl ether **29**, probably via a common cyclic cationic intermediate which undergoes ring opening stereospecifically.

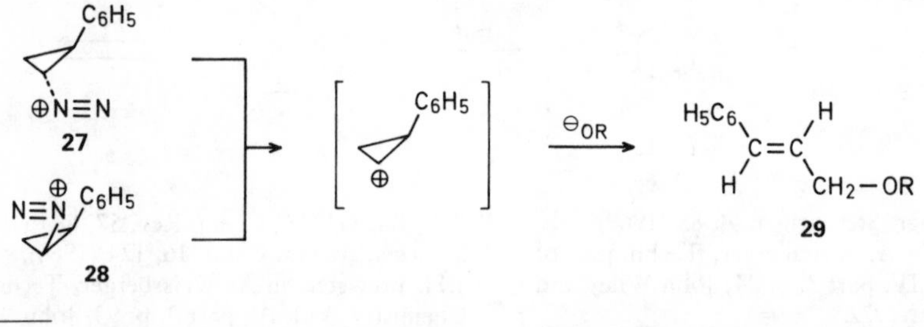

[74] A. Wasserman, Diels Alder reaction, Elsevier, Publ. Co., Amsterdam, New York, 1965; J.C. Martin and R.K. Hill, Chem. Rev. **61**, 537 (1961); N'Guyen Trong Anh, Les règles de Woodward-Hoffmann, p. 89–98, 100, Ediscience, Paris, 1972.

[75] H.R. Nace, Organic Reactions **12**, 57 (1962); R.F.W. Bader and A.N. Bourns, Can. J. Chem. **39**, 348 (1961).

[76] D.J. Cram and J.E. McCarty, J. Amer. Chem. Soc. **76**, 5740 (1954).

3.3. Creation of Relative Stereochemistry

3.3.1. Asymmetric Inductions

With reactions carried out on a molecule which contains an asymmetric center, the relative configuration of the generated compound will be induced from the configuration of the element of chirality already present. Important empirical rules have been advanced in many cases by Cram[82] and by Cornforth[80] for the 1,2-asymmetric inductions in acyclic ketone additions, by Felkin[83] for cyclic and acyclic ketone reactions, and by Prelog for the 1,4-asymmetric induction[84].

3.3.2. Diastereogenic Reactions

This topic refers to reactions by which molecules which are devoid of chirality elements are converted into *threo-erythro* or *E,Z*-diastereoisomers. When two neighboring asymmetric centers are created simultaneously in the reaction, *a,a*-diastereogenic formation of a C–C bond occurs according to the definition proposed by Schlosser[85]. Many additions in which aldehyde and ketone groups participate are diastereogenic reactions and the *threo* or *erythro*-isomers that are formed can either be isolated or stereoselectively transformed into the *E,Z*-olefins. Consider, for example, the stereochemistry of betaine formation in the initial step of the Wittig reaction between a phosphorus ylid and an aldehyde[86] where the following rules apply:

(i) under conditions of kinetic control, the reaction of ylids with aldehydes mainly yields the *erythro*-betaines;

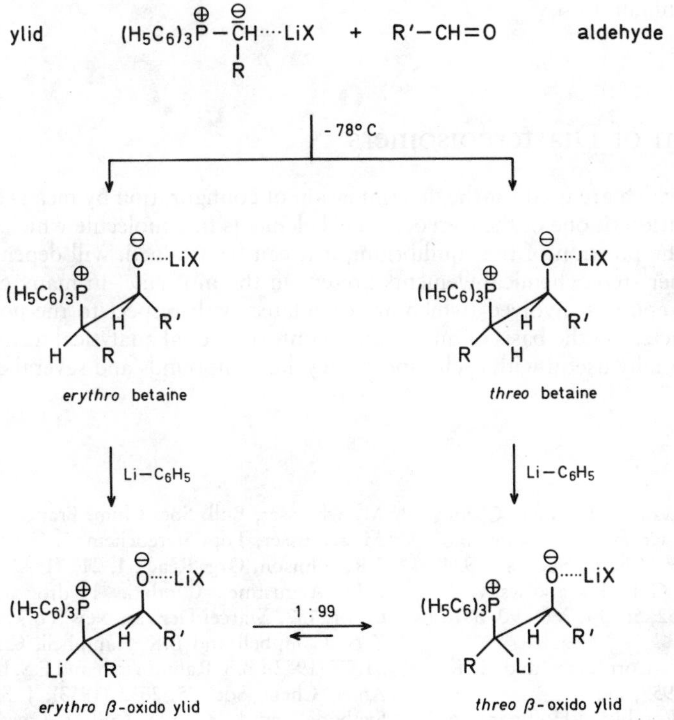

ylid $(H_5C_6)_3\overset{\oplus}{P}-\overset{\ominus}{\underset{R}{CH}}\cdots LiX$ + $R'-CH=O$ aldehyde

$-78°C$

erythro betaine

threo betaine

$Li-C_6H_5$

$Li-C_6H_5$

erythro β-oxido ylid

1 : 99

threo β-oxido ylid

(ii) under equilibrating conditions and in the presence of lithium salts, formation of the *threo* betaines is favored.

[77] A.C. Cope and E.M. Acton, J. Amer. Chem. Soc. 80, 355 (1958).

[78] J. Reucroft and P.G. Sammes, Quart. Rev. Chem. Soc. 25, 135 (1971).

The predominant isomer obtained in the Perkin condensation is that in which the Ar and COOH groups are *trans*[87].

$$Ar-CHO \quad + \quad (R-CH_2-CO)_2O \quad \xrightarrow{\text{base}} \quad \begin{array}{c} Ar \\ \diagup \\ H \end{array} C=C \begin{array}{c} R \\ \diagdown \\ COOH \end{array}$$

Alkynes are excellent precursors for the synthesis of olefins and the addition of a reagent Y–H to the C ≡ C bond give either the *E*- or *Z*-isomer of the olefin depending on the stereochemistry of the reaction involved. Thus, catalytic reduction of alkynes gives almost exclusively the *cis* isom-

$$R-C\equiv C-R' \quad + \quad Y-H \quad \begin{cases} \xrightarrow{\text{cis-addition}} & \begin{array}{c} R \\ \diagup \\ H \end{array} C=C \begin{array}{c} R' \\ \diagdown \\ Y \end{array} \\ \\ \xrightarrow{\text{trans-addition}} & \begin{array}{c} R \\ \diagup \\ H \end{array} C=C \begin{array}{c} Y \\ \diagdown \\ R' \end{array} \end{cases}$$

er[88], while reduction by sodium in liquid ammonia gives the *trans*-isomer[89]. Reduction by diborane, disiamylborane[90] or diisobutylaluminum hydride[91] affords the *cis*-olefin. Additions of thiols[92] or methanol[93] to alkynes proceed in a *trans* manner and yield vinylic thioethers and enol ethers of well defined configuration.

3.4. Equilibration of Diastereoisomers

In general, the methods which are used for the determination of configuration by means of equilibration involve epimerization of one of the stereochemical elements in a molecule which contains several such elements. The position of the equilibrium, if it can be attained, will depend on the configurations of the other stereochemical elements present in the molecule. In many cases, the relative stabilities of the epimers involved (which are calculated with respect to the position of equilibrium) can be predicted on the basis of quantitative conformational analytical techniques[94]. Such procedures are especially useful with cyclic and polycyclic compounds and several examples are given below.

[79] E.J. Corey and R.A.E. Winter, J. Amer. Chem. Soc. **85**, 2677 (1963); E.J. Corey, F.A. Carey, and R.A.E. Winter, J. Amer. Chem. Soc. **87**, 934 (1965); E.J. Corey and G.T. Kwiatkowsky, J. Amer. Chem. Soc. **88**, 5652, 5653 (1966); **90**, 6816 (1968).

[80] J.W. Cornforth, R.H. Cornforth and K.K. Mathew, J. Chem. Soc. **1959**, 112.

[81] N'Guyen, Les règles de Woodward-Hoffmann, p. 15–75, Ediscience, Paris, 1970.

[82] D.J. Cram and F.A. Abd Elhafez, J. Amer. Chem. Soc. **74**, 5828 (1952).

[83] M. Cherest and H. Felkin, Tetrahedron Lett. **1968**, 6127.

[84] J. Morrison and H.S. Mosher, Asymmetric Organic Reactions, p. 55–83, Prentice Hall, Englewood, New York, 1971.

[85] M. Schlosser, Bull. Soc. Chim. France **1971**, 453.

[86] M. Schlosser, Top. Stereochem. **5**, 1 (1970).

[87] J.R. Johnson, Org. React. **1**, 210 (1942).

[88] R.L. Augustine, Catalytic Hydrogenation, p. 62–71, 152, Marcel Dekker, New York, 1965.

[89] K.N. Campbell and B.K. Campbell, Chem. Rev. **31**, 77 (1942); B.S. Rabinovitch and F.S. Looney, J. Amer. Chem. Soc. **75**, 2652 (1953); J. Sicher, M. Svoboda and J. Zavada, Collect. Czech. Chem. Commun. **30**, 421 (1965).

[90] H.C. Brown and G. Zweifel, J. Amer. Chem. Soc. **83**, 3834 (1962).

[91] G. Wilke and H. Muller, Chem. Ber. **89**, 444 (1956).

[92] W.E. Truce and J.A. Simms, J. Amer. Chem. Soc. **78**, 2756 (1956).

[93] S.I. Miller, J. Amer. Chem. Soc. **78**, 6091 (1956).

Cyclohexanols R–OH can be equilibrated either with the isopropyl alcohol/isopropoxide system in acetone[95] or with Raney nickel[96]. Alternatively, these alcohols can be epimerized by use of a mixture of lithium aluminum hydride and aluminum chloride, which can be advantageous in that it is not only the free alcohol which is equilibrated but also the alcoholate RO–AlCl$_2$. The complexed oxygen function in the alcoholate RO–AlCl$_2$ is very bulky and hence will be essentially *equatorial*. The position of the equilibrium will then depend exclusively on the positions, nature and configurations of the other substituent groups in the cyclohexanol. The role of the latter can be evaluated from tables of conformational free energy differences (A-values[97]).

| 29 | 30 |

Cholestane-2a,3a-diol **29**, for example, can be epimerized in basic medium to the more stable diequatorial diol **30**. The other two possible diols (2β, 3β and 2β, 3a) can also be equilibrated to **30**, and hence the stereochemistry of **30** is established.

There are precautions which must be observed in the use of equilibration methods, notably that the equilibrium should actually be reached (absence of secondary reactions); this can normally be verified by equilibration of mixtures of different compositions.

Stereomutation of olefins can be effected thermally in the presence of a catalyst; it is generally readily predictable[98], that the more stable isomer is formed in excess. Photochemical isomerization techniques, on the other hand, often give mixtures in which the thermodynamically less stable isomer predominates[98].

[94] E.L. Eliel, N.L. Allinger, S.J. Angyal, and G.A. Morrison, Conformational analysis, Wiley Intersci. Publ., New York, 1965.

[95] E.L. Eliel and H. Haubenstock, J. Org. Chem. **26**, 3504 (1961).

[96] G. Chiurdoglu and W. Masschelein, Bull. Soc. Chim. Belges **70**, 767 (1961).

[97] E.L. Eliel, Stereochemistry of Carbon Compounds, p. 236. Mc Graw-Hill Book Co., New York, 1962.

[98] J.H. Brewster in A. Weissberger, Techniques of Chemistry, Vol. IV, part 3, p. 18–19, John Wiley and Sons, New York, 1972.

Prelog's Method

J.C. Fiaud
Laboratoire de Synthèse Asymétrique, Université de Paris-Sud, Orsay, France

The reactions of achiral reagents with chiral keto esters have been reviewed by Morrison and Mosher[1]. This contribution is concerned with the applications of reactions of this type to the determination of absolute configuration; the topics covered are as follows:

Table of Contents

1.   The Prelog Rule: Definition and Illustration

In 1953, Prelog[2] put forward an empirical rule whereby the absolute configuration of an optically active secondary alcohol which had been utilized for a reaction proceeding via asymmetric induction could be related to the absolute configuration of the enantiomer of the a-hydroxy acid which was ultimately obtained as the product of the synthesis. The overall synthetic scheme is outlined in Scheme 1 (Fischer projections are used throughout this chapter; the abbreviations L, M and S for large, medium and small refer to the substituents on the asymmetric carbon atom of the alcohol, and are assigned on the basis of relative size according to the classification proposed by Cram[3]). Esterification of an a-keto acid 1 with an optically active alcohol 2 – the absolute configuration of only one of the enantiomers is shown – gives an optically active a-keto ester 3. Treatment of this ester with an achiral reagent such as an organometallic derivative or hydrogen results in formation

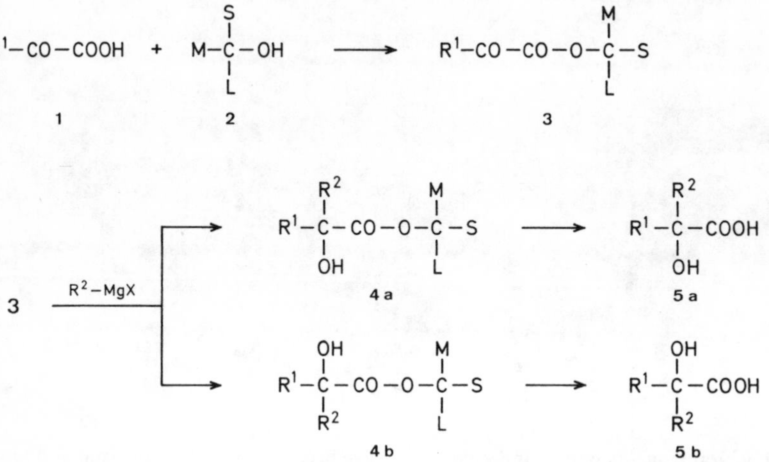

Scheme 1

of the diastereomeric a-hydroxy esters 4, from which the enantiomeric a-hydroxy acids 5 may be obtained by hydrolysis. The acid 5 will be optically active if, during the reaction sequence, the asymmetry of the alcohol has resulted in the formation of different amounts of 4a and 4b.

This type of reaction was investigated[4-8] and the results obtained formed the basis on which Prelog, by analysis of the steric course of reaction and consideration of the absolute configurations of the compounds involved, developed his rule. An analogous steric analysis could, however, not be performed before Prelog as knowledge of conformational analysis was non-existent in those days and the absolute configurations of the compounds with which the chemists worked were unknown[4].

Prelog systematically studied the influence of the nature of the alcohol employed on the absolute configuration of the product obtained in the asymmetric synthesis, and assumed that there is a correlation between asymmetric induction and the relative size of the substituent groups which are located nearest to the trigonal atom undergoing reaction. On the basis of this assumption, he then formulated an empirical rule which defines the relationship between the configuration of the

[1] J.D. Morrison and H.S. Mosher, "Asymmetric Organic Reactions", p. 53, 80, Prentice Hall, Englewood Cliffs N.J., 1971.

[2] V. Prelog, Helv. Chim. Acta **36**, 308 (1953); V. Prelog, Bull. Soc. Chim. France **1956**, 987.

[3] D.J. Cram and F.A.A. Elhafez, J. Amer. Chem. Soc. **74**, 5828 (1952).

[4] A. McKenzie, J. Chem. Soc. **85**, 1249 (1904); **87**, 1373 (1905); **89**, 365 (1906).

[5] A. McKenzie and H. Wren, J. Chem. Soc. **89**, 688 (1906); **95**, 544 (1909).

[6] A. McKenzie and B.P. Humphries, J. Chem. Soc. **95**, 1105 (1909).

enantiomer of the α-hydroxy acid which is preferentially formed and that of the alcohol used as inducing agent. This rule is illustrated in Scheme 2.

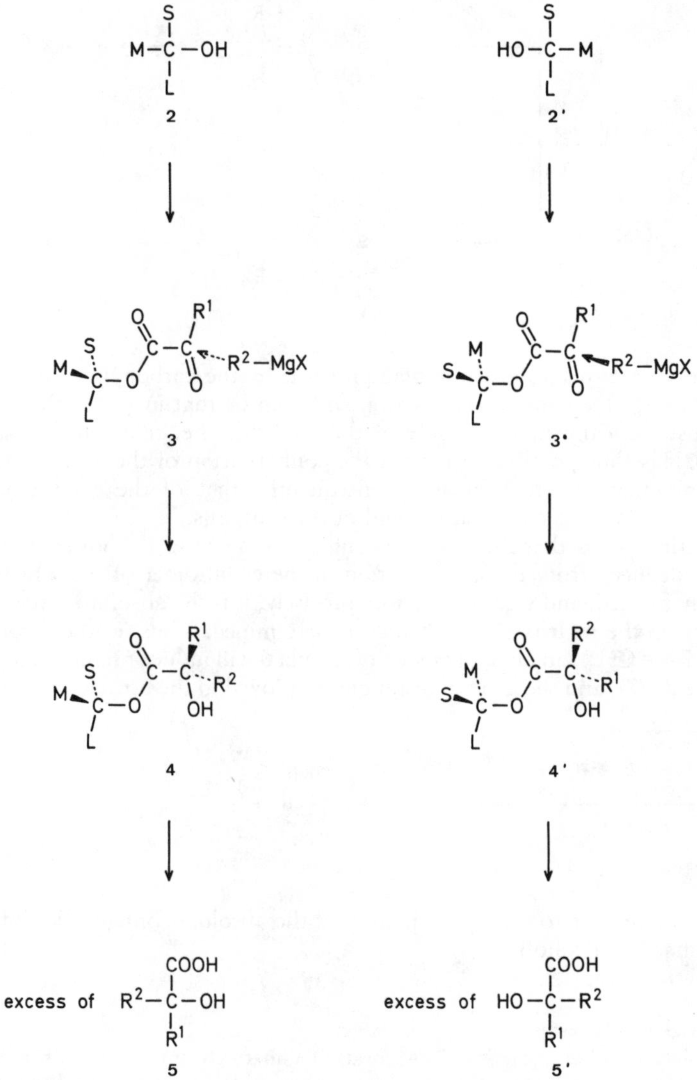

Scheme 2

The alcohol **2** with the configuration as shown, should lead to preferential formation of the α-hydroxy acid **5**; conversely, if alcohol **2′** is employed in the synthesis, the enantiomeric α-hydroxy acid **5′** should be preferentially formed. Similarly, reaction of R^1–MgX with R^2–CO–CO–O–C(LMS) and of R^2–MgX with R^2–CO–CO–O–C(LMS) should lead to enantiomeric α-hydroxy acids.

---

[7] A. McKenzie and P.D. Ritchie, Biochem. J. **231**, 412 (1931); **237**, 1 (1931); **250**, 376 (1932).   [8] A. McKenzie and E.W. Christie, Biochem. J. **277**, 426 (1935).

Prelog has justified this precise analysis of the steric course of reaction on the basis of conformational analysis. If the most favorable conformation of the a-keto ester in the transition state is that shown in Scheme 3, in which the two carbonyl groups are antiparallel, then the substituent groups

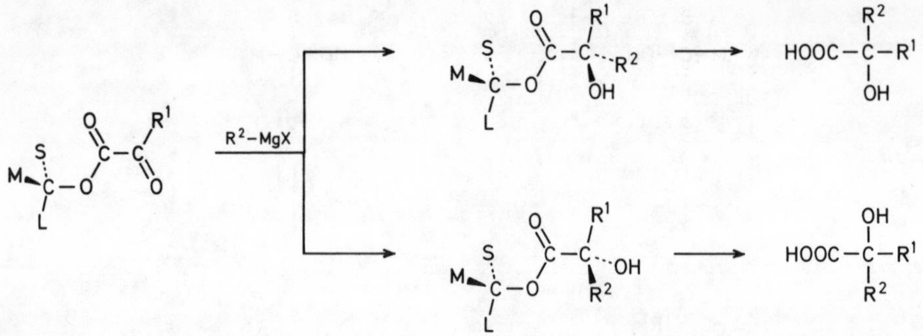

Scheme 3

M and S will be located on either side of the plane formed by the carbonyl groups. The most favorable transition state for the subsequent reaction will then be that in which the reagent approaches from the least sterically hindered side of the molecule, i.e. that which contains the smallest substituent S. It is thus possible to predict the configuration of the asymmetric carbon atom which will be preferentially formed and, consequently, that of the enantiomer of the a-hydroxy acid which is isolated in excess at the end of the synthesis.

The practical value of this rule is that the absolute configuration of the alcohol employed as the inducing agent can be deduced from the configuration of the enantiomer of the a-hydroxy acid which is predominantly formed, and vice versa. More precisely, it is the absolute configuration of the carbon atom carrying the hydroxy group which is determined. Thus, in the atrolactic acid synthesis ($R^1 = C_6H_5$, $R^2 = CH_3$), an alcohol of stereoformula 6 will induce preferential formation of (S)-(+)-atrolactic acid[9] (7), and the general technique employed in the atrolactic acid synthesis

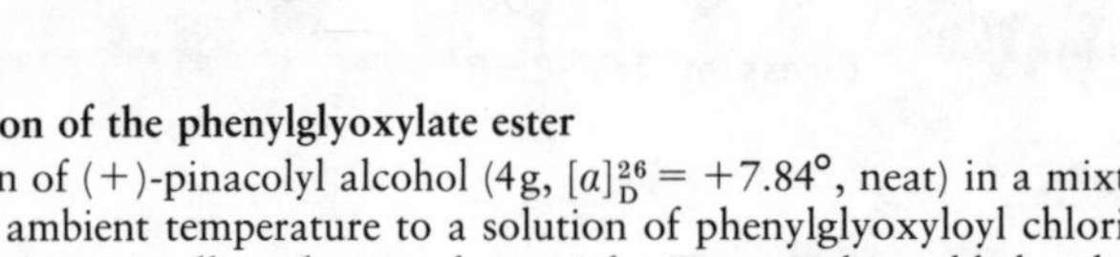

is illustrated below with reference to the determination of the absolute configuration of (+)-3,3-dimethyl-2-butanol (pinacolyl alcohol).

Preparation of the phenylglyoxylate ester

A solution of (+)-pinacolyl alcohol (4g, $[a]_D^{26} = +7.84°$, neat) in a mixture of pyridine and benzene (2:3) is added at ambient temperature to a solution of phenylglyoxyloyl chloride[12] in anhydrous benzene, and the reaction mixture is allowed to stand overnight. Water is then added and the mixture extracted with ether. The organic phase is separated, washed with aqueous acetic acid, water and then dried. Evaporation of the ether gives 7.3 g of the ester.
b.p. 101°/0.2 mm; $[a]_D^{21} = +12.4°$ (c 3.8, ethanol).

Asymmetric Synthesis

A solution of the ester (0.5 g) in anhydrous ether is added dropwise to a solution of methylmagnesium iodide (6–7 mmol) in anhydrous ether at 0°; the solution is stirred for 2 hr at ambient temperature and then for 1 hr under reflux. The resulting clear solution is hydrolyzed with cold dilute acetic acid, extracted with ether, and the ethereal extract dried and evaporated under reduced pressure. The mixture of atrolactate esters thus obtained is hydrolyzed with a 5% solution of potassium hydroxide in methanol by heating under reflux under nitrogen for 5 hr. The methanol is evaporated, the residue dissolved in water, and the alkaline solution extracted with ether. The aqueous layer is then acidified with hydrochloric acid and extracted several times

with ether; these ether extracts are combined, dried, and evaporated under reduced pressure to give crude
(S)-(+)-atrolactic acid (0.29g)
$[a]_D^{21} = +8.7°$ (c 7.6, ethanol)[13]; optical purity 23%[10].

Interpretation

As dextrorotatory (S)-atrolactic acid (7) is the predominant enantiomer formed in the synthesis, (+)-pinacolyl
alcohol must have the stereoformula 6. Assignment of S, M and L to H, CH_3 and $(CH_3)_3C$, respectively, and
application of the Cahn, Prelog and Ingold sequence rules shows that for this enantiomer the configuration is S^{11}.

2.   Attempts at Rationalization of the Prelog Rule

Many attempts have been made to rationalize the steric course of the Prelog asymmetric synthesis
via a-keto esters, and to provide a theoretical basis for the empirical rule previously discussed. It is
known that the asymmetric synthesis of the a-hydroxy ester takes place under conditions of kinetic
control, and that the rate determining step of the reaction is in fact conversion of the a-keto ester
into the corresponding a-hydroxy ester. Ideally, solution of the problem would necessitate detailed
information both of the transition state conformations and of the free energy difference between
the diastereoisomeric transition states, and such information on the reacting substrate molecule is
not available. Consequently, known ground state properties have been utilized in analyses of
model systems where the steric situation is believed to approximate to that which occurs during
reaction. The atrolactic acid synthesis in particular has been discussed in these terms. Many
analyses of the conformation of the reacting phenylglyoxylate ester have been discussed in these
terms. Numerous analyses of the conformation of the reacting phenylglyoxylate molecule have
been carried out where a "reactant like" transition state (8) has been assumed:

8

One important point with respect to the interpretation of the steric course of the reaction is the
configuration around the 2–3 bond, i.e. the relative orientation of the two carbonyl groups. Prelog
assumed in his model that the two carbonyl groups were antiparallel as in 8 but it is now known
that this is probably not the most stable conformation of the a-keto ester. X-ray crystallographic
studies of the 4-bromophenylglyoxylate ester of (–)-menthol, for example, have shown that the
dihedral angle between the two carbonyl groups is 104°; this conformation may also exist in
solution[14]. Nevertheless, it is believed[1] that the antiparallel arrangement of the carbonyl groups
is certainly realized in the transition state as this leads to a better distribution of substrate charge
density under the influence of the reagent.
In analogous reactions involving a symmetric synthesis with imines 9, however, interpretation
of the steric course of the reactions has been made on the basis of a s-cis configuration of the C = N

[9] The absolute configuration of (–)-atrolactic acid
has been correlated to the absolute configuration of
d-(+)-glyceraldehyde[10] and is S according to the
Cahn, Ingold and Prelog nomenclature[11].

[10] K. Freudenberg, J. Todd, and R. Seidler, Justus
Liebigs Ann. Chem. 501, 199 (1933).

[11] R.S. Cahn, C.K. Ingold, and V. Prelog, Experien-
tia 12, 81 (1956); Angew. Chem. Int. Ed. 5, 385
(1966).

[12] H.C. Brown and M.S. Karash, J. Amer. Chem.
Soc. 64, 329 (1942).

[13] The specific optical rotatory power of enantiomerically pure atrolactic acids is $[a]_D = 37.7°$ (ethanol).

[14] R. Partasarathy, J. Ohrt, A. Horeau, J.P. Vigneron, and H.B. Kagan, Tetrahedron 26, 4705
(1970).

and C = O groups. Thus, in the hydrogenation of the imines of a-keto acids, esters or amides, it has been assumed that, because of factors such as coordination of the heteroatoms of the substrate

9

X = NH−R,OR,OH

with the metal, these molecules adopt the *s-cis* configuration[15-17].
In the Prelog model 8, the 2,3-, 3,4- and 4,5-bonds are represented as being coplanar, and it is in fact now known, both from dipole moment studies[18] and from microwave spectroscopy[19], that esters of the type RCOOR' do adopt a planar configuration and that the CO and OR' groups are *cisoid* (10). If this hypothesis is accepted, then three conformations for the alcohol substituent groups must be considered (11 A–C). From examination of the mode of attack of the reagent, it can be seen

10   11 A   11 B   11 C

that only conformations **11 A** and **11 B** will lead to the same enantiomer of the a-hydroxy acid as that indicated by Prelog; the third conformation **11 C** will give the antipode. However, analyses such as this which are based only on one conformer are not accurate as they deal only with the difference in the relative steric bulk of the S and M substituents, and neglect the relative size of L. Consequently, it has been attempted to provide a semi-quantitative estimate of the optical yield during application of the Prelog rule by taking into account the probability of existence of the three rotamers **11 A–C**[20]. Thus, the high asymmetric induction (66%) observed with the phenylglyoxylate ester of a-methyl 2,4,6-tricyclohexylbenzyl alcohol[21] can be explained on the basis that conformation **11 B** is significantly preferred over conformations **11 A** and **11 C**, which are destabilized relative to **B** because of the considerable steric interactions between the ester C=O group and the substituents at positions 2 and 6 in the benzene ring. The differences in extent of asymmetric induction with menthol and neomenthol[22] have been interpreted similarly as have Prelog's observations[23] that induction is generally less with *axial* than with *equatorial* cyclohexyl phenylglyoxylates. As a result of these analyses, the authors have forwarded the hypothesis that the relative energy levels generated owing to interactions present in the various rotamers of the initial keto ester are not inverted, but are maintained in the corresponding transition states.
Prelog[2] suggested a method for calculation of the amount of asymmetric induction in the atrolactic acid synthesis. In this method, which has been discussed in detail[24], the three eclipsed conforma-

[15] A. Kanai and S. Mitsui, C.A. **65**, 16835g (1966).

[16] K. Harada and T. Yoshida, Bull. Soc. Chim. Japan **43**, 921 (1970).

[17] E. Frainnet, P. Braquet, and F. Moulines, C.R. Acad. Sci., Paris **272**, 1435 (1971).

[18] J.M. Sturtevant, J. Amer. Chem. Soc. **55**, 4478 (1933); C.T. Zahn, Trans. Faraday Soc. **30**, 304 (1934); R.B.J Marsden and L.E. Sutton, J. Chem. Soc. **1936**, 1383; M.L. Bender, Chem. Rev. **60**, 53 (1960).

[19] J.M. Ogorman, W. Schand, and V. Schomaker, J. Amer. Chem. Soc. **72**, 4222 (1950); R.F. Curl, J. Chem. Phys. **30**, 1529 (1959).

[20] J. Weill-Raynal and J. Mathieu, Bull. Soc. Chim. France **1969**, 115.

[21] V. Prelog, E. Philbin, E. Watanabe, and M. Wilhelm, Helv. Chim. Acta **39**, 1086, (1956).

[22] V. Prelog and H.L. Meier, Helv. Chim. Acta **36**, 320 (1953).

[23] W.R. Feldman and V. Prelog, Helv. Chim. Acta **41**, 2396 (1958).

[24] R. Bentley, "Molecular Asymmetry in Biology", Vol. 1, p. 102, Academic Press, 1969.

tions of the phenylglyoxylate ester, denoted by i, are considered. To each is assigned a term h_i, which is a measure of the fraction of the total molecules of the keto ester which have conformation i, and a factor S_i, which is a measure of the difference in steric crowding of the two diastereotopic faces of the molecule with respect to attack by the reagent. Then, for conformation i, when (+)-atrolactic acid is formed in excess, $O < S(+)_i < 1$; when (−)-atrolactic acid is formed in excess, $O < S(+)_i < 0.5$. The factor $q(+)$, which is a measure of the final predominance of the (+)-form, is given by

$$q(+) = \sum_{i=1}^{3} S(+)_i h_i$$

with

$$\sum_{i=1}^{3} h_i = 1$$

and the percentage of the (+)-ester formed $p(+)$ is given by

$$p(+) = (2q(+) - 1) \times 100.$$

It has been postulated that, in a reaction which proceeds via two diastereoisomeric transition states (Scheme 4) and in which a new asymmetric center C′ is created under the influence of an

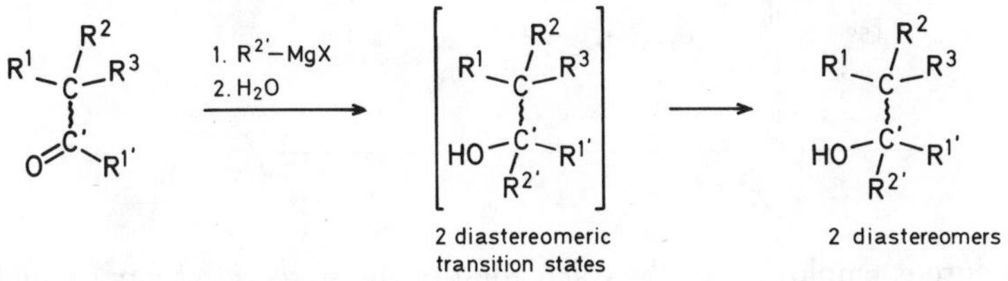

Scheme 4

asymmetric center C already present, the ratio of diastereomeric product P and N can be calculated on the basis of a relationship similar to that in the Hammett equation[25]:

$$\Delta(\Delta G^{\ne}) = - RT \log \frac{KRR'}{KRS'} = - RT \log Q = f(X, X')$$

R, S = configuration of the inducing alcohol
R', S' = configuration of the atrolactic acid produced

χ and χ' are the chirality functions associated with the inducing asymmetric carbon atom and the asymmetric carbon atom being formed, and are of the form

$$\chi = (\lambda_1 - \lambda_2)(\lambda_2 - \lambda_3)(\lambda_3 - \lambda_1)$$

where λ_i are ligand parameters which only depend on the nature of the ligand. For a given reaction such as the atrolactic acid synthesis, the asymmetric carbon atom which is formed has the same substituents $R^{1'}$, $R^{2'}$ and $R^{3'}$ (OH, C_6H_5 and CH_3, respectively) and thus χ' can be represented by a constant τ. The relationship then becomes

$$\log Q = \delta \tau \chi$$

where τ is a valid constant for a given reaction at a given temperature, and δ, the value of which is +1 or −1, indicates the sense of the asymmetric induction (see below). On the basis of experimental results obtained in the atrolactic acid synthesis, and by adoption of the arbitrary values $\lambda_H = 0.00$ and $\lambda_{CH_3} = 1.0$, Ugi and Ruch have determined the value of τ for the atrolactic acid synthesis and has calculated the λ values for a number of substituent groups (Table 1).

Table 1: λ values for the three different substituents at the asymmetric carbon atom of **8** (see Table 3).

R	λ_R	R	λ_R
H	0.00	1– naphthyl	1.29
CH_3	1.00	Bornyl	1.86
C_2H_5	1.05	$(H_5C_6)_3C$	1.75
C_3H_7	1.08	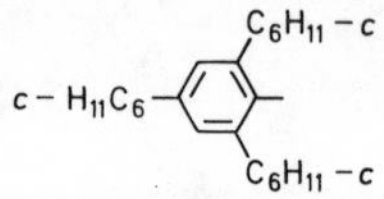 $c-H_{11}C_6$ ⟨ring with $C_6H_{11}-c$ and $C_6H_{11}-c$⟩	2.10
$CH(CH_3)_2$	1.27	OH	0.83
$C(CH_3)_3$	1.49	H_3CO-	0.80
C_6H_5	1.23	$H_3C-CO-O-$	0.75
cyclohexyl	1.33	H_5C_2O-CO-	0.90
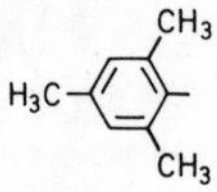 H_3C-⟨ring with CH_3, CH_3⟩	1.58	$H_5C_2O-CO-CH_2-$	1.10

The following procedure is employed for the calculation of the stereoselectivity of an atrolactic acid synthesis, and for the prediction of the configuration of the alcohol which is used. The alcohol is drawn in the Newman projection, with the OH group to the rear, and the remaining substituents then assigned normally. If the resulting configuration is R, δ is assigned the value $+1$, and if it S, the value -1. Calculation of the chirality function χ then requires evaluation of

$$\chi = (\lambda_1 - \lambda_2)(\lambda_2 - \lambda_3)(\lambda - \lambda_1)$$

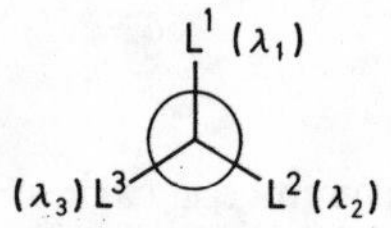

where λ_1, λ_2 and λ_3 are set equivalent to the indices L^1, L^2 and L^3, assigned in a clockwise fashion in the Newman projection. The sign of the product $\delta\chi\tau$ is independent of the configuration of the alcohol; the sign of the expression $\log C_P/C_N$ is given in Table 2.

Table 2: Sign of $\log C_P/C_N$

		Configuration of the atrolactic acid produced	
		R'	S'
Configuration of the inducing alcohol	R	$+$	$-$
	S	$-$	$+$

The configuration of the alcohol is that for which the expressions $\delta\chi\tau$ and $\log C_P/C_N$ have the same sign.

Consider for example the case of 3,3-dimethyl-2-butanol, which, in the atrolactic acid synthesis, leads to (S)-(+)-atrolactic acid of the optical purity 23%. The value of τ for the atrolactic acid synthesis is 0.30, and if the alcohol is represented as in p. 26 (i.e. the R configuration), then

$$\delta = 1, \ \chi = (1.00 - 1.49)(1.49 - 0.00)(0.00 - 1.00) = +0.73$$

hence, $\delta\chi\tau = +0.219$. This expression is positive, the configuration of the atrolactic acid obtained is S, and hence, by inspection of Table 2, it can be seen that the configuration of (+)-3,3-dimethyl-2-butanol is S.

Data for a number of other examples are summarized in Table 3.

Table 3: Calculated and observed Asymmetric Inductions for the Atrolactic Synthesis of the Ruch-Ugi linear free Enthalpy Method.

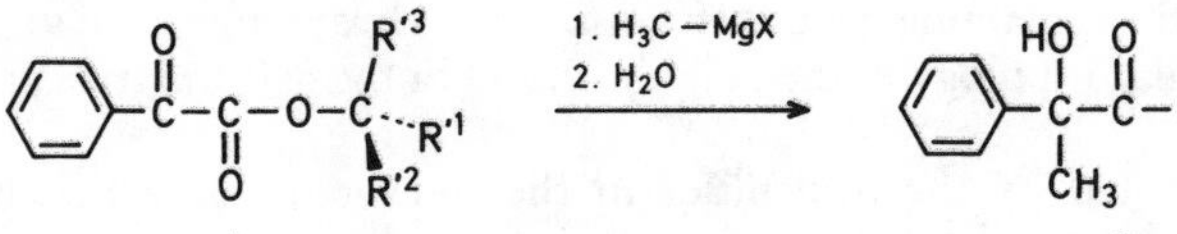

Substituents of 8			Ligand Constants			Chirality Function χ	Mol-% (R, R) – 8a		Configuration	
R¹	R²	R³	λ_1	λ_2	λ_3		Calc.[a]	Found	Pred.	Found
H	CH₃	(H₃C)C	0	1.00	1.49	+0.730	62.4	62.0	S	S
H	CH₃	C₆H₅	0	1.0	1.23	+0.283	55.0	51.5	S	S
H	CH₃	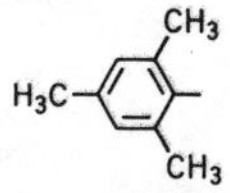 H₃C—⟨CH₃/CH₃⟩	0	1.00	8.58	−0.918	65.4	65.0	R	R
H	CH₃	1-naphthyl	0	1.00	1.29	+0.375	56.3	56.0	S	S
H	CH₃	(+)-bornyl	0	1.00	1.86	+1.60	75.2	77.0	S	S
H	CH₃	(H₅C₆)₃C	0	1.00	1.75	−1.31	71.3	74.5	R	R
H	CH₃	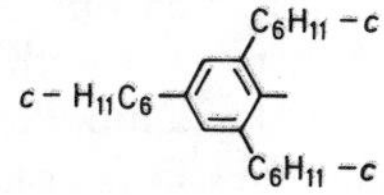 c-H₁₁C₆—⟨C₆H₁₁-c/C₆H₁₁-c⟩	0	1.00	2.10	−2.30	83.2	83.0	R	R
H	C₆H₅	(+)-bornyl	0	1.23	1.86	+1.44	73.1	70.5	S	S
H	C₆H₅	(H₅C₆)₃C	0	1.23	1.75	−1.12	68.4	63.5	R	R

[a] Calculated for value $\tau = 0.30$.

[25] I. Ugi, Chimia 19, 91 (1965); E. Ruch and I. Ugi, Top. Stereochem. 4, 99 (1969).
a) $K_{RR'}$, and $K_{RS'}$, designate the rate constants of the formation of RR' and RS' diastereomeric esters.

[26] M. Kawana and S. Emoto, Bull. Chem. Soc. Japan 40, 2168 (1967); 41, 259 (1968).

3.   Problems Arising from the Application of the Prelog Rule. Limitations

3.1.   Assignment of the Priority Order L, M, S to the Substituents on the Asymmetric Carbon Atom of the Alcohol

Correct application of the Prelog rule obviously requires that the priority order L, M, S be properly assigned to the substituent groups of the asymmetric carbon atom in the inducing alcohol on the basis of the relative steric bulk of these groups. Prelog has stated that the rule is strictly valid only when all of the alcohol substituents are alkyl groups[2]. In cases where one of the substituent groups carries a center of unsaturation or a heteroatom, however, assignment of priority can generally be made unambiguously. Particular care should however be exercised in cases where hereroatoms are present as the conformational distribution can then be significantly influenced by complex formation between the heteroatom and metal salts or organometallic compounds which are present in the reaction medium. In asymmetric syntheses with alcohols which contain several asymmetric centers, induction mainly occurs via the asymmetric carbon atom which carries the OH group, and in these cases, priority classification of substituents can generally be accomplished by examination of the degree of substitution of the remaining groups. Even so, it is always advisable in such cases to examine the complete molecular topology in the neighborhood of the asymmetric carbon atom prior to final assignment.

These considerations are illustrated by the difficulties in the interpretation which have been described in atrolactic acid syntheses where sugar derivatives have been employed as inducing agents[26]. Thus, when the synthesis was carried out with 1,2:5,6-di-isopropylidene-(a)-D-glucose, (R)-(–)-atrolactic acid was obtained, and if L is assigned as the lateral chain of the sugar, application of the Prelog rule to **12** clearly indicates that the (R)-(–)-acid should be formed. Examination of models of the phenylglyoxylate conformation, as recommended by Prelog for the prediction of the

12

steric course of the reaction, reveals however that the front side of the molecule is sterically shielded by the L substituent. Consequently, approach of the reagent should be from the rear side, and this should lead to the formation of (S)-(+)-atrolactic acid. In order to resolve this apparent anomaly and justify formation of the (–)-acid, Kawana and Emoto resorted to a modified but valid Prelog model in which interactions between the bulky L substituent and the CO ester group could be avoided. They postulated that the O–C bond of the ester and the C=O bond were no longer coplanar, but that the O–C bond was directed to the rear of the molecule, thus opening the front side to approach of the reagent (see **13**).

13   **13 A**   **13 B**   **13 C**

Similar difficulties in interpretation have been described[27] with respect to the atrolactic acid synthesis carried out with 7,8-dihydrocodeine, which gives 10% of (R)-$(-)$-atrolactic acid of optical purity 15%. The three conformations for the phenylglyoxylate ester are shown in 13 A–13 C. If the priority order is assigned as C-5 = R_L, C-7 = R_M, and H = R_S, then the Prelog rule predicts formation of (S)-$(+)$-atrolactic acid. This in turn corresponds to preferential attack of the reagent on the rear side of conformers 13 A and 13 B, and on the front side of conformer 13 C. Examination of models shows, however, that

(a) conformation A is highly unfavorable
(b) attack of the reagent on conformer 13 C should take place at the front rather than at the rear side of the molecule because of the methoxy group.

In order to explain the preferential formation of (S)-$(+)$-atrolactic acid the authors were forced to assume that attack of the reagent occurred mainly at the rear side of conformer C rather than at the rear side of conformer B.

3.2.   Anomalies of and Exceptions to the Prelog Rule

When the atrolactic acid synthesis is carried out with 3β-cholestanol (14), (R)-$(-)$-atrolactic acid is obtained in 1.7% enantiomeric excess[2]. Examination of models with respect to priority assign-

14

ment of the substituent groups indicates that the steric crowding at C-2 is greater than at C-4. If the assignment is made on this basis, however, then the (S)-$(+)$-acid should be preferentially formed. Thus, as far as the stereochemical analysis is concerned, the case of 3β-cholestanol appears to be an exception to the rule; the observed asymmetric induction is however so low that no firm conclusion can be drawn from these results.
Utilization of either $(-)$-15 a or $(+)$-15 b epicatechin tetramethylether in the atrolactic acid synthesis leads to preferential formation of (R)-$(-)$-atrolactic acid[28]. These two compounds are however

15 a   15 b

epimeric at C-3 and thus should give enantiomeric atrolactic acids. Once again, however, the low stereoselectivity of the reaction using 15 b and the presence of the oxygen atom close to the inducing center imply that the correct conditions for the application of the Prelog rule are not fulfilled. Consequently, this result must be considered as an anomaly rather than an exception to the rule.
For analogous reasons, namely the presence of fluorine atoms, the Prelog rule cannot be properly applied to the phenylglyoxylate esters of trifluoromethylcarbinols[29].

[27] K.W. Bentley and H.M.E. Cardwell, J. Chem. Soc. 1955, 3252.
[28] A.J. Birch, J.W. Clark-Lewis, and A.V. Robertson, J. Chem. Soc. 1957, 3586.
[29] J.A. Dale, Ph. D. Thesis, Stanford University, 1970.

3.3.   Complex Molecules

Direct determination of the absolute configuration of some complex molecules may prove either difficult or impossible because of the nature of the functional groups present, or because of a lack of a suitable functional group with which to operate. In such cases, it may prove either necessary or desirable to transform the substrate into a derivative which can be more readily analyzed – as for example, conversion into an alcohol, which can then be cycled in the atrolactic acid synthesis. Thus, the absolute configuration at C-11 of a-santonine 16 has been elucidated by transformation into 17 as shown in Scheme 5 and subsequent application of the Prelog method to this derivative[30].

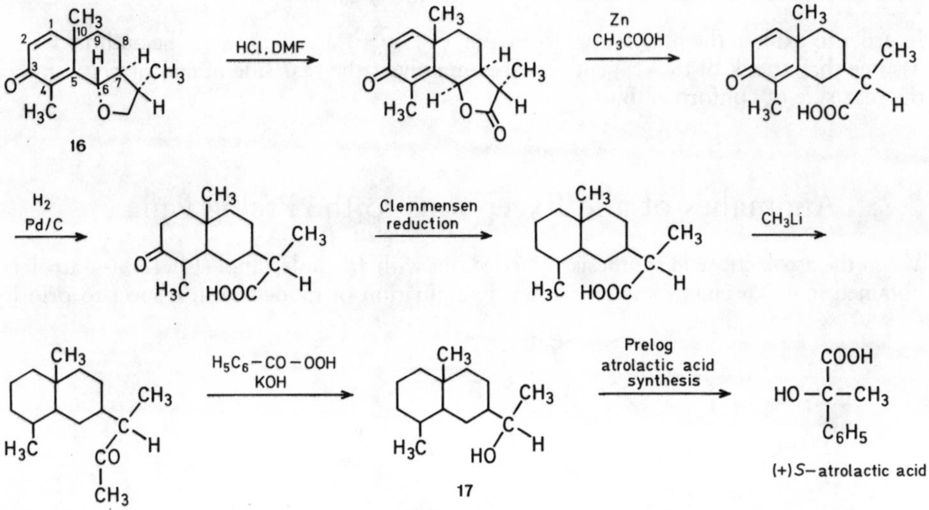

Scheme 5

As (S)-$(+)$-atrolactic acid has been obtained at the end of this process, the configuration at C-11 in 17, and hence in 16, is S.

The absolute configuration of $(-)$-citrinine 18 has been deduced in an analogous fashion from the configuration of the hydrolysis product 19 and the corresponding dimethyl ether 20[31].

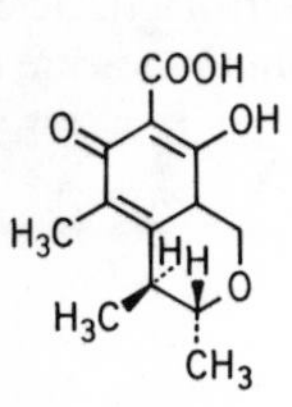

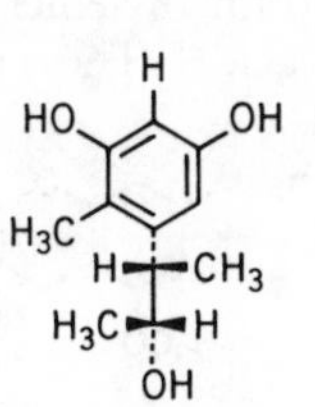

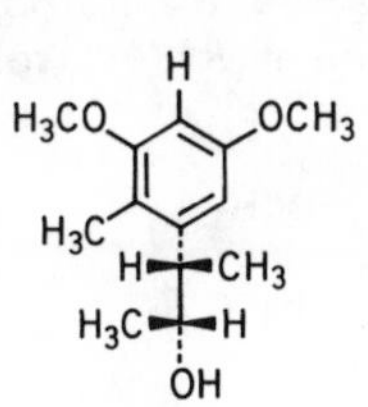

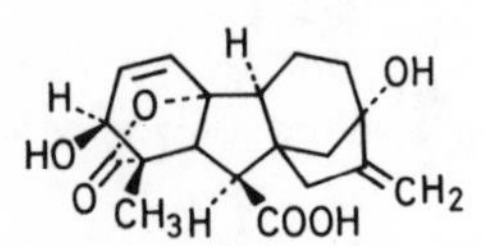

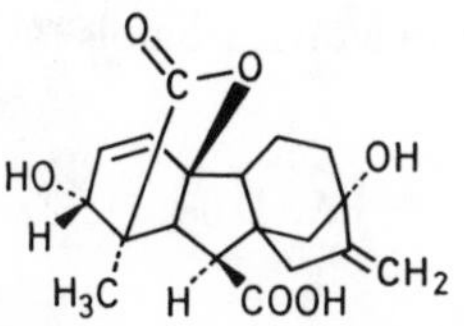

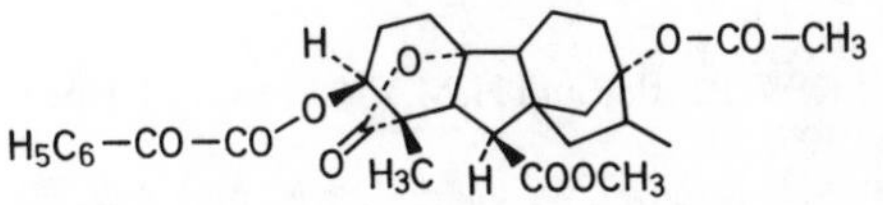

Similarly, the question of the orientation of the lactone ring in gibberellic acid has been settled; structures 21 and 22 have previously been proposed for this acid. Treatment of the methyl ester of gibberellic acid with a mixture of phenylglyoxylyl chloride and isopropenyl acetate gives 23, which, on reaction with methylmagnesium iodide in tetrahydrofuran affords *(S)-(+)-*atrolactic acid, thus showing that the configuration at C-3 is *S*. This result excludes **22** and confirms **21** as the absolute configuration of gibberellic acid[32].

3.4.   Axially Dissymmetric Molecules

The atrolactic acid synthesis can be of particular value in the assignment of absolute configuration to molecules which exhibit biphenyl-type chirality. The atrolactic acid synthesis has also been carried out with 1-(1-naphthyl)-2-naphthol **24** and (+)-phenyldihydrothebaine **25**, both of which show *axial* chirality[33]. Both phenols give *(R)-(−)*-atrolactic acid, with very high stereoselectivities (85 and 93%, respectively). Strictly speaking, the Prelog rule cannot be applied in these cases for the prediction of configuration of the atrolactic acid formed, as the hydroxy group in each com-

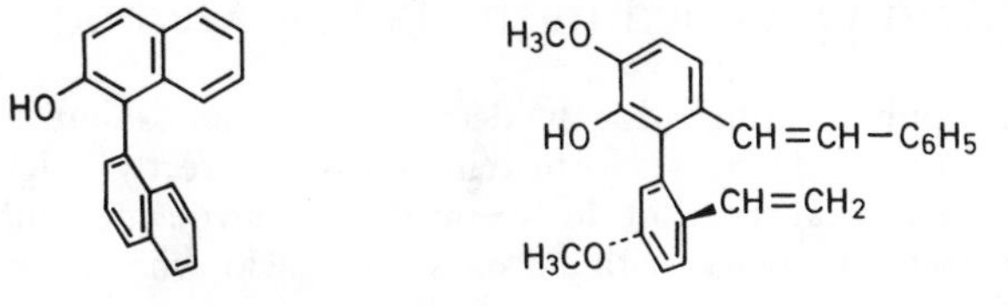

24   **25**

pound is phenolic. Nevertheless, interpretation of the asymmetric synthesis can be made in terms of shielding and compression effects. The authors assume that the most stable ground state conformation of the keto ester in the phenylglyoxylate derivative of **25** is that in which the carbonyl groups are *coplanar* and *transoid* (**25 A**). The most stable disposition of this chain with respect to the biphenyl system is that in which the plane of the two carbonyl groups is perpendicular to

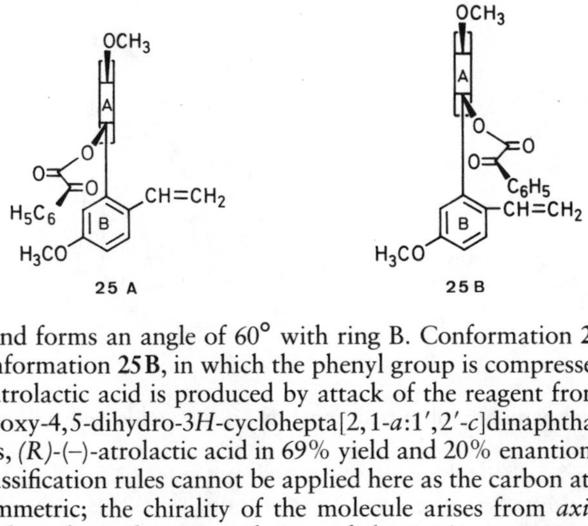

25 A   **25 B**

ring A and forms an angle of 60° with ring B. Conformation **25 A** is assumed to be more stable than conformation **25 B**, in which the phenyl group is compressed against the vinyl group. Hence, *(R)-(−)*-atrolactic acid is produced by attack of the reagent from the top of the molecule.
4β-Hydroxy-4,5-dihydro-3*H*-cyclohepta[2,1-*a*:1′,2′-*c*]dinaphthalene (**26**) gives, on atrolactic acid synthesis, *(R)-(−)*-atrolactic acid in 69% yield and 20% enantiomeric excess[34]. The normal substituent classification rules cannot be applied here as the carbon atom carrying the hydroxy group is not asymmetric; the chirality of the molecule arises from *axial* asymmetry (atropoisomerism). Nevertheless, from the point of view of the steric congestion around the hydroxy group, the

[30] Y. Abé, T. Miki, M. Sumi, and T. Toga, Chem. and Ind. (London) **1956**, 953.

[31] P.P. Mehta and W.B. Whalley, J. Chem. Soc. **1963**, 3777.

[32] S. Masamune, J. Amer. Chem. Soc. **83**, 1515 (1961).

[33] J.A. Berson and M.A. Greenbaum, J. Amer. Chem. Soc. **80**, 445 (1958); **80**, 653 (1958).

[34] K. Mislow, V. Prelog, and H. Scherrer, Helv. Chim. Acta **41**, 1410 (1958).

naphthalene residue on the seven-membered ring proves to have the larger steric requirement. Consequently, the alcohol **26** corresponds to the stereoformula **27** and hence induces formation of (R)-(–)-atrolactic acid.

26   **27**

3.5. Determination of the Absolute Configuration and Optical Purity of the α-Hydroxy Acid Obtained in the Prelog Method

It is obvious that the Prelog rule can only be utilized for the determination of absolute configuration if the configuration of the α-hydroxy acid which is formed in excess is correctly assigned. This may be done by measurement of the optical rotation: for example, (+)-atrolactic acid has the absolute configuration S. It is advisable to work with pure, isolated acid when making such measurements as this avoids possible contamination by optically active impurities, and hence unreliable results.

It should be noted that the absolute configuration of the atrolactic acid which is formed need not necessarily be determined by polarimetric methods but may be obtained by examination of the NMR spectrum of a solution of the corresponding methyl ester in dextrorotatory 1-(1-naphthyl)-ethylamine. It has been shown[35] that in this solvent the ester methyl group of (–)-methyl atrolactate resonates at higher field than the corresponding methyl group of the (+)-isomer (chemical shift difference, $\Delta\delta = 0.9\,Hz$; see Fig. 1).

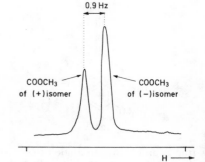

Fig. 1: Relative field position of methoxycarbonyl resonances in the ¹H-NMR spectrum of methyl atrolactates.
$[\alpha]_D^{26} = -7.95°$ (c 4.4 C_2H_5OH); (21% e.e.)
Solvent: (+)-1-(1-naphthyl)ethylamine

The amount of atrolactic acid which is finally obtained depends on the yields realized in each of the three steps involved, namely
3.5.1. the asymmetric synthesis; 3.5.2. hydrolysis of the α-hydroxy ester; 3.5.3. isolation and purification of the α-hydroxy acid. Moreover, the degree of enantiomeric excess observed in the final product is a direct consequence of the degree of enantiomeric purity of the asymmetric carbon atom which is formed in the first stage of the synthesis. Various problems can be encountered at each step in the synthesis; these are discussed below, together with recommended procedures which may be employed to minimize the effects arising from such problems.

[35] W.H. Pirkle and S.D. Beare, Tetrahedron Lett. **21**, 2579 (1968).

[36] W.G. Dauben, D.F. Dickel, O. Jeger, and Y. Prelog, Helv. Chim. Acta **36**, 325 (1953).

3.5.1. Asymmetric Synthesis

Theoretically, methylmagnesium iodide can react with either of the two electrophilic centers in the phenylglyoxylate ester, namely the ketonic carbonyl group, which leads to the formation of the diastereoisomeric a-hydroxy esters **28**, and the ester carbonyl group, which leads to the formation of the achiral ketol **29** (Scheme 6). Furthermore, use of excess of Grignard reagent results in the formation of the enantiomeric diols **30**, which can arise either from the esters **28** or from the ketol

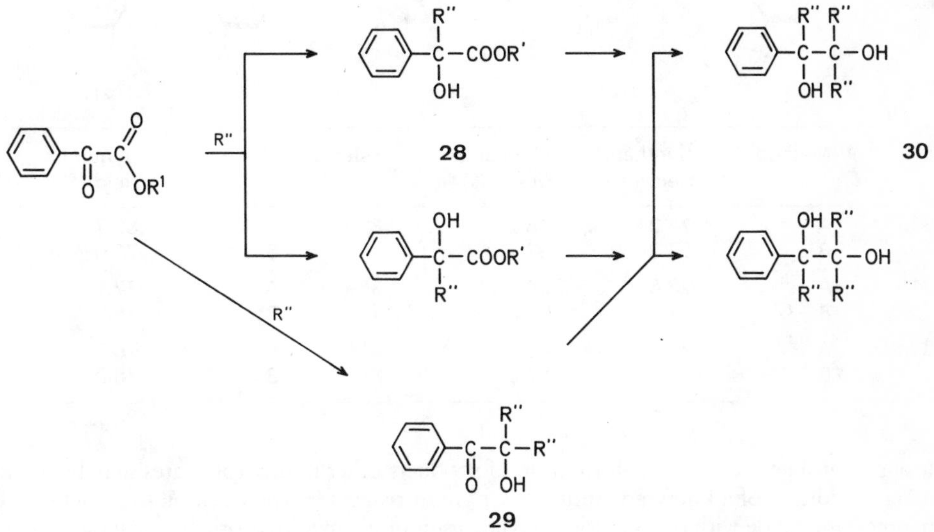

Scheme 6

29. It is obvious that those reactions which result in the production of either **29** or **30** or both will lead to a lower yield of the desired a-hydroxy acid **28** ($R' = H$). In practice, however, the ketol **29** has never been isolated as a reaction product, and it is generally accepted that in the atrolactic acid synthesis reaction of the Grignard reagent with the ketonic carbonyl group is much faster than with the ester carbonyl group. Consequently, the only secondary reaction which has been observed is the slow formation of the diol **30** via the diastereomeric a-hydroxy esters **28**.

Specific procedures have been recommended for control of this secondary process. Prelog suggested direct addition of the a-keto ester to the Grignard reagent: a solution of the a-keto ester (0.5 M) is added to a solution of the Grignard reagent in anhydrous ether (1–2 M solution) cooled to 0°. The reaction mixture is stirred at ambient temperature for 1 hr and at reflux for a further 0.5 hr; the cooled reaction mixture is then hydrolyzed with cold dilute acetic acid and the ethereal layer separated, washed with water, dried and evaporated.

In a work on carbohydrate esters, slightly modified conditions have been used[26]: "An ethereal solution of the sugar ester is added during 5 min. to a solution of methylmagnesium iodide (3 mol. equiv.) at −5 to 0° with stirring. After stirring for another 5 min., the diastereomeric mixture is treated with ammonium chloride, and the resulting atrolactate is hydrolyzed..." (Method A). To ensure minimization of attack on the two diastereoisomeric esters by excess of Grignard reagent, the authors used a slightly modified procedure in parallel control experiments: "...the ethereal solution of the sugar ester is added during a longer period (40 min.), with stirring for an additional 1 hr..." (Method B).

If the a-hydroxy esters are indeed involved in a secondary reaction with excess Grignard reagent, then the synthetic yield of a-hydroxy acids should be different by the two methods. As can be seen from examination of the data in Table 4, the yield difference for the two methods never exceeds 10%.

Table 4: Asymmetric synthesis of *(S)*-atrolactic acid with sugar derivatives[26]

Ester	Method	Synthetic Yield (%)	Optical Yield (%)	Ester	Method	Synthetic Yield (%)	Optical Yield (%)
31a	A	72.2	38.2	**31d**	A	80.7	25.2
	B	67.8	37.4		B	72.0	26.0
31b	A	78.6	34.2	**31e**	A	77.1	22.0
	B	77.4	32.6		B	75.3	21.8
31c	A	77.4	28.1	**31f**	A	78.3	30.5
	B	69.6	27.6		B	76.9	29.2

It has been suggested that the formation of products other than atrolactates may be minimized by inverse addition of a known quantity of Grignard reagent[33]. The work on the reaction of methylmagnesium iodide with the phenylglyoxylate ester of phenyldihydrothebaine in particular allows a comparison to be made of the chemical yield of atrolactic acid as a function of molar ratio of Grignard reagent to ester (Table 5).

Table 5: Reaction of methylmagnesium iodide with the phenylglyoxylate ester of phenyldihydrothebaine[33].

Molar Ratio: CH_3Mg I/phenylglyoxylate	Atrolactic Acid	
	Chemical Yield %	Optical Yield %
1.00	78	71
1.25	67	70

From the data in Table 5 it appears that, in order to obtain a good yield of atrolactic acid, it is preferable to use only a stoichiometric amount, or slight excess, of Grignard reagent relative to the phenylglyoxylate ester. If an insufficient amount of Grignard reagent is employed, reaction with the ester will be incomplete and the atrolactic acid which is obtained will be contaminated with phenylglyoxylic acid. This α-keto acid can easily be detected in the reaction product by use of 2,4-dinitro-phenylhydrazine reagent (to which, of course, the atrolactic acid is inert) and is not normally a particularly troublesome contaminant provided that the rotation of the atrolactic acid is significant.

As previously mentioned, the secondary reaction whereby the diastereoisomeric atrolactate esters react further with Grignard reagent leads to a decrease in the yield of isolated atrolactic acid. The same secondary process may also modify the enantiomeric composition of the asymmetric center which is formed. This situation arises if each of the diastereoisomers **32** does not react with the excess Grignard reagent at the same speed. Thus, if $k_1 = k_2$, the optical purity of the 1,2-diols **33** should be the same as that of the atrolactic acid obtained from the synthesis. If $k_1 \neq k_2$, however, 33 will be optically active and the optical purity of the isolated atrolactic acid will not correspond

H₃C, OH   H₃C, OH   H₃C OH   H₃C OH CH₃
    C   →k₁   C CH₃   C   →k₂   C—C—OH
H₅C₆ COOR   H₅C₆ C—OH   H₅C₆ COOR   H₅C₆ CH₃
                      CH₃

   32 a   33 a   32 b   33 b

to the asymmetric yield of the atrolactic acid synthesis. The extent of this secondary reaction and its influence on the value of the optical purity of the isolated atrolactic acid can be determined by comparison of the optical purities of the acid and diol with the amounts of each that are obtained.

Prelog has studied this problem in the case of 17β-androstanyl phenylglyoxylate[36]. The atrolactic acid recovered at the end of the synthesis has a specific rotation of $[a]_D = +6.2°$, while the neutral fraction from the reaction – probably the diol – has a specific rotation of $[a]_D = -0.46$[37]. Treatment of the methyl ester of the atrolactic acid, which has been isolated, with methylmagnesium iodide give a glycol with a specific rotation of $[a]_D = +4.0°$. This result clearly proves that methylmagnesium iodide reacts more rapidly with the 17β-androstanyl ester of $R(-)$-atrolactic acid than with the corresponding ester of the enantiomeric acid. Consequently, from the results obtained in the actual atrolactic acid synthesis, it can be seen that in this particular case effective formation of the asymmetric carbon of S configuration has been achieved in the asymmetric synthesis.

3.5.2. Hydrolysis of the a-Hydroxy Ester

It is essential at this stage of the operation to ensure that hydrolysis of the diastereoisomeric atrolactate esters proceeds to completion. This apparently obvious precaution has not always been observed, however, and it has been shown[2] that some asymmetric syntheses, in which the results did not conform to the rule, have simply been incorrectly carried out experimentally. The source of error in these cases was incomplete hydrolysis of the esters, which led to false values for the induced asymmetry. Thus, a laevorotatory acid has been obtained[27] by hydrolysis of the a-hydroxy ester prepared by treatment of (–)-menthyl naphthylglyoxylate with phenylmagnesium bromide; in a subsequent reinvestigation of this reaction, however, Prelog showed that, when hydrolysis was allowed to go to completion, the dextrorotatory acid was obtained. In a similar reinvestigation of some of McKenzie's earlier work, Prelog demonstrated that complete hydrolysis of the ester formed by treatment of (+)-bornyl phenylglyoxylate with isobutylmagnesium bromide gave a (–)-acid and not, as had been observed by McKenzie, a (+)-acid; the (+)-acid was in fact shown to be derived from the ester prepared from (–)-borneol.

3.5.3. Isolation and Purification of the a-Hydroxy Acid

Optical rotation measurements are normally carried out with the crude atrolactic acid, which is isolated by standard methods. Purification of the acid, for example, by recrystallization, is not generally advisable as this may result in some optical enrichment of one of the enantiomers. The same is true for most normal methods of purification, although sublimation has been occasionally employed.

It follows that the greater the optical purity of the isolated atrolactic acid, the more reliable will be the assignment of the absolute configuration of the inducing alcohol. Application of the Prelog rule requires that the rotation of the a-hydroxy acid be significant and, in the particular case of the atrolactic acid synthesis, the optical purity of the isolated acid should be greater than 5%[1]. There are two main reasons for this criterion, one experimental and the other theoretical. Firstly, atrolactic acid with an optical purity of 5% has a specific rotation of 2°; under the normal experimental concentration conditions, this is equivalent to an observed rotation of 0.1°, which is rather small (even though modern polarimeters are accurate to 0.002°). Secondly, an asymmetric induction of 5% corresponds to two reactions in which the difference in activation energy is only 0.05 kcal mol^{-1}. This energy difference is so small that it cannot be accurately related to the factors involved in the asymmetric synthesis even though these appear in competitive reactions which occur in the same reaction medium between reagents which have the same energy.

Material balance should always be checked before and after hydrolysis and in cases where a low yield of a-hydroxy acid is obtained, the reason for it should be determined. Thus, it is possible to find out whether a poor material balance is due to a genuine secondary reaction such as those discussed earlier, or merely to incomplete ester hydrolysis. If the former case applies, the glycol product should be isolated and its rotation measured.

3.5.4. Calculation of Optical Yield Using *racemic* Mixtures

It is possible in many cases to calculate the enantiomeric purity of the asymmetric carbon atom which is synthesized simply by measurement of the relative proportions of diastereoisomers which are formed. This value will be identical to the optical purity of the a-hydroxy acid which is isolated, provided that no optical enrichment has occurred during hydrolysis and isolation.

The value of the enantiomeric purity of the asymmetric carbon atom which is formed can be determined by examination of the a-hydroxy esters which are obtained when the Grignard reagent is allowed to react with the a-keto ester of the *racemic* alcohol[1, 38]. Its magnitude will also correspond to the absolute value of the maximum optical purity which can be expected for the a-hydroxy acid obtained from the analogous synthesis in which an optically pure alcohol has been employed. Thus, on the assumption that it is necessary to isolate an a-hydroxy acid of an optical purity greater than 5%, and the above test carried out with a *racemic* alcohol, this will indicate, a priori

(a) whether the determination of absolute configuration by the Prelog method is feasible, and

(b) if so, the required minimum optical purity of the alcohol in question in order to obtain, in the proper asymmetric synthesis, an a-hydroxy acid with an optical purity over 5%. Consider, for example, an atrolactic acid synthesis carried out with the phenylglyoxylate ester of a racemic alcohol, and assume that the relative proportion of diastereoisomeric a-hydroxy esters obtained corresponds to an asymmetric yield (expressed as the amount of asymmetric induction) of 20%. This result clearly establishes that the Prelog method will be both applicable and reliable in this case provided that the atrolactic acid synthesis is carried out with an alcohol of optical purity greater than $5 \times 100/20 = 25\%$. If so, then the optical purity of the isolated atrolactic acid would be expected to be in the range 5–20%.

4. Atrolactic Acid Synthesis and Determination of the Absolute Configuration of Secondary Alcohols

The atrolactic acid synthesis and the Prelog rule have been widely used for the determination or confirmation of absolute configuration of secondary alcohols. The relevant data are summarized in Table 6, in which the alcohols are classified according to type, viz. aliphatic alcohols, alicyclic alcohols, monoterpene alcohols and related compounds, sesquiterpene alcohols and related compounds, triterpene alcohols, steroid alcohols, alkaloids and alkaloidal constituents, sugars and related compounds, miscellaneous alcohols, and biphenyls and binaphthyls (*axial* asymmetry or atropisomers). The compounds within each category are arranged in the order of increasing molecular formula. For each alcohol the following data, when available, is given: the configuration (either already known, or determined by the atrolactic acid synthesis, and subsequently confirmed by other methods if necessary); the optical yield in the asymmetric synthesis (calculated from the optical purity of the atrolactic acid isolated); the chemical yield; and the appropriate references.

Table 6.

	Alcohol ROH			Atrolactic Acid		
No.	Compound	Conf.[a] Obs.	Pred.	Optical Yield %	Chemical Yield %	Ref.

Acyclic Alcohols

No.	Compound	Conf.[a] Obs.	Pred.	Optical Yield %	Chemical Yield %	Ref.
1	(+)-3,3-dimethyl-2-butanol	$S^{c, d}$	S	24	82	[21]
2	(−)-1-phenylethanol	S	S	3	78	[21]
3	(−)-2-octanol	R	R	18	43	[5] (1909)h [7] (237, 1, 1931)h
4	(+)-1-(2,4,6-trimethylphenyl)ethanol	R	R	30	82	[21]
5	(−)-1-(1-naphthyl)ethanol	S	S	12	90	[21]
6	(−-3-(3,5-dimethoxy-2-methylphenyl-phenyl)-2-butanol	R^{d}	R	37	80	[31]
7	(−)-1,1,1-triphenyl-2-propanol	R	R	49	−	[21]
8	(+)-1,2,2,2-tetraphenylethanol	R	R	27	85	[21]
9	(+)-1-(2,4,6-tricyclohexylphenyl)ethanol	R	R	60	75	[21]
10	(−)-methadol	S^{d}	S	73	81	[39]

| 11 | (−)-isomethadol | R^{d} | R | 25 | 67 | [40] |

[37] The specific rotation of (R)-(−)-phenylethylene glycol has been shown to be $[a]_D^{25} = -39.7°$ (c 4.33, 95%, C_2H_5OH), $[a]_D^{25} = -63.7$ (c 5.5, $CHCl_3$; J.A. Dale and H.S. Mosher, J. Org. Chem. 35, 4002 (1970).

[38] J.C. Fiaud, and A. Horeau, Tetrahedron Lett. 1972, 2565.

[39] P.S. Portoghese and D.A. Williams, J. Med. Chem. 12, 839 (1969);

[40] P.S. Portoghese and D.A. Williams, J. Med. Chem. (b) 13, 626 (1970).

Table 6. (continued)

	Alcohol ROH		Atrolactic Acid			
No.	Compound	Conf[a]	Conf.	Optical Yield %	Chemical Yield %	Ref.

Cyclic Alcohols

| 12 | 1(S)-9(S)-trans-1-decalol 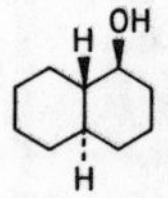 | S[d] | S | 15 | 82 | 7 (1932)h |

| 13 | 1(S),9(R)-trans-1-decalol 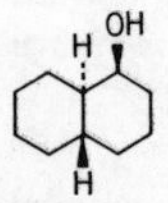 | S[d] | S | 2 | 100 | 7 (1932)h |

| 14 | 1(S), 8(S)-cis-8-methylhydrindanol 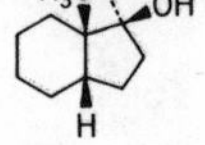 | S[d] | S | 16 | 75 | 41 |
| | | S | S | 16 | 90 | 41 |

| 15 | 1(S), 8(R)-cis-8-methylhydrindanol 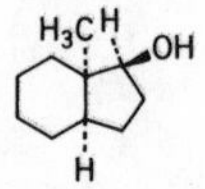 | S[d] | S | 12 | 94 | 41 |

| 16 | 5(S), 8(S)-cis-8-methylhydrindanol 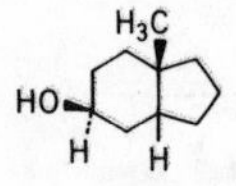 | S[d] | S | 6 | 62 | 41 |

| 17 | octahydrodeacetyllaurencin 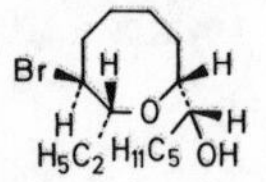 | R[d] | S | 17 | 83 | 42 |

Terpene Alcohols and Related Compounds

| 18 | (−)-borneol 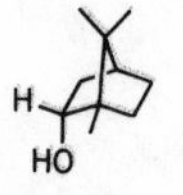 | R | R | 5 | 77 | 4 (1906)h |
| | | R | R | 4 | 90 | 4 (1906)h |

Table 6. (continued)

No.	Compound	Conf[a]	Conf.	Optical Yield %	Chemical Yield %	Ref.
	Alcohol ROH			Atrolactic Acid		
19	(+)-borneol 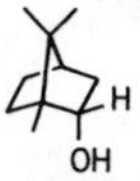	S	S	11	90	22
20	(−)-isoborneol 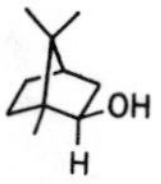	R	R	8	98	22
21	(−)-menthol 	R	R	22	—	4 (1905)h
		R	R	25	—	4 (1905)h
		R	R	23	79	4 (1906)h
		R	R	25	97	22
		R	R	29	30	43
		R	R	29	77	26
		R	R	30	78	26
22	(+)-neomenthol 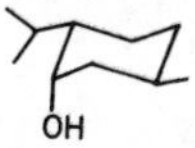	S	S	12	94	22
23	(−)-1-bornylethanol 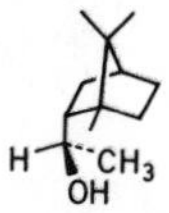	S[d]	S	54	90	44
24	(−)-1-bornyl-1-phenylmethanol 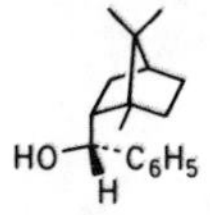	R[d]	S	41	72	44

Sesquiterpene alcohols and related compounds

| 25 | 11-noreusantan-11-ol 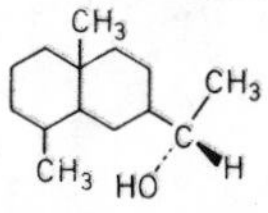 | S[d] | S | 15 | — | 30 |

Table 6. (continued)

	Alcohol ROH			Atrolactic Acid		
		Conf.[a]		Optical	Chemical	Ref.
No.	Compound	Obs.	Pred.	Yield %	Yield %	

Triterpene alcohols

| 26 | euphol 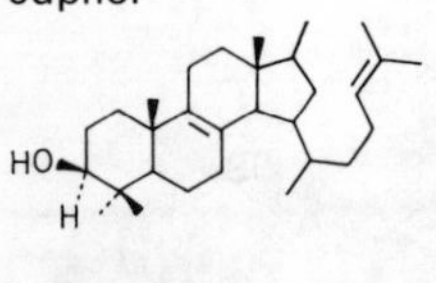 | S[b] | S | 24 | 69 | [45] |

| 27 | α-amyrin 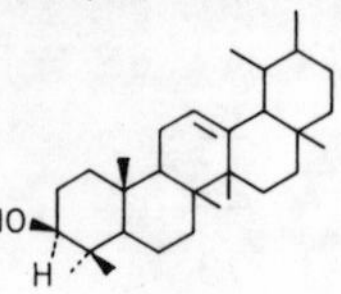 | S[b] | S | 10 | 71 | [45] |

| 28 | 5α-Lanosta-8, 17 (20) dien-3β-ol-(dihydrolanosterol) 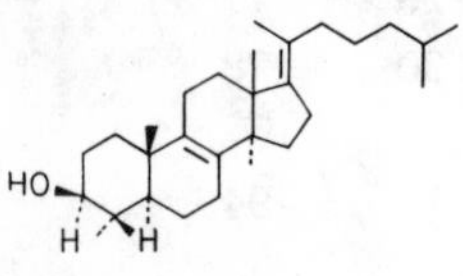 | S[d] | S | 34 | 58 | [45] |

Steroids

| 29 | 17β-androstanol 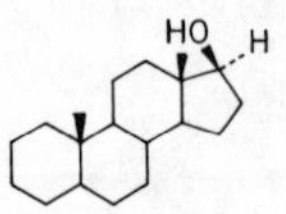 | S | S | 16 | 45 | [45] |

| 30 | 5α-pregnan-20β-ol 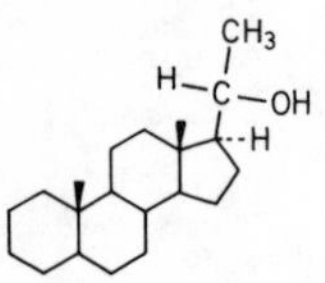 | R | R | 52 | 91 | [46] |

| 31 | 5α, 17α-pregnan-20α-ol 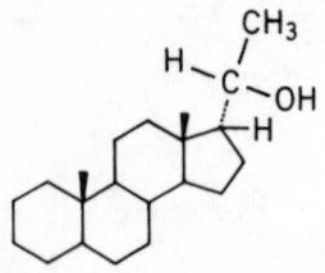 | S | S | 18 | 85 | [47] |

Table 6. (continued)

	Alcohol ROH		Atrolactic Acid			
No.	Compound	Conf.[a] Obs.	Pred.	Optical Yield %	Chemical Yield %	Ref.
32	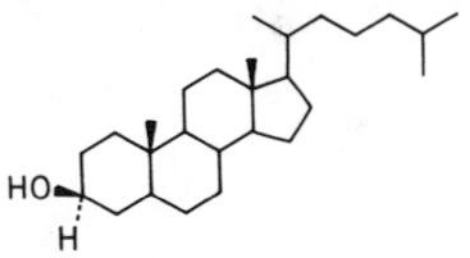 3β-cholestanol	S	R	2	82	45
33	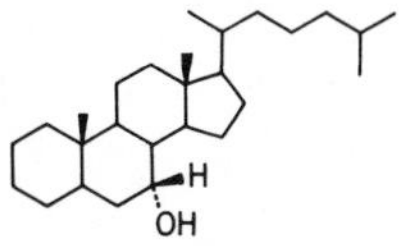 7α-cholestanol	R	R	13	93	45
34	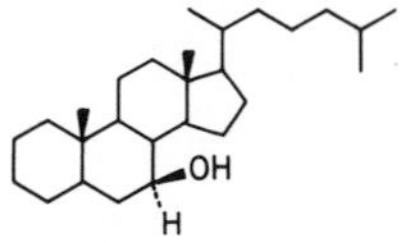 7β-cholestanol	S	S	69	86	45
35	22α-hydroxy-3-methoxy-5-cholestene	R	S	18	70	48
		R[e]	R	4	86	49
36	22β-hydroxy-3-methoxy-5-cholestene	R	R	33	52	48
		S[e]	S	32	76	49

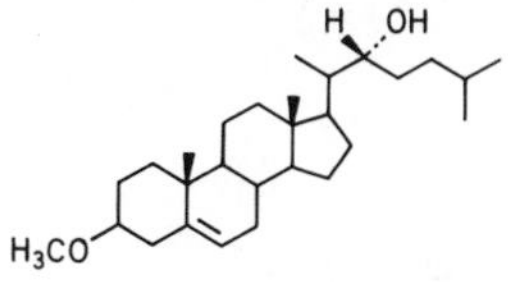

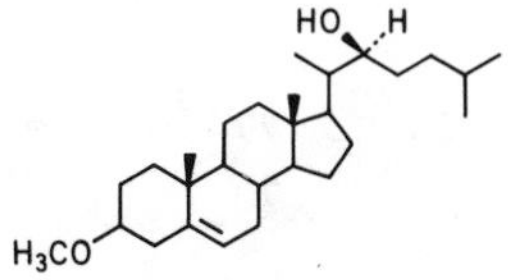

Alkaloids and Alkaloid Constituents

37	dimethyl-jaconecate 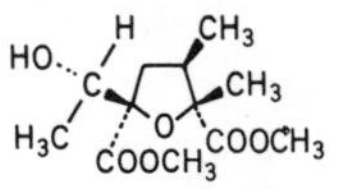	S[d]	S	11	60	50

Table 6. (continued)

| No. | Compound | Conf[a] | | Atrolactic Acid | | Ref. |
		Obs.	Pred.	Optical Yield %	Chemical Yield %	
38	dihydrocodeine 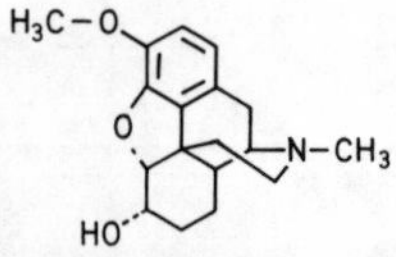	S^d	R	15	10	27

39	yohimbine 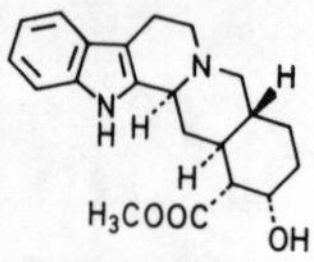	S	S	4	—	51

40	methyl reserpinate 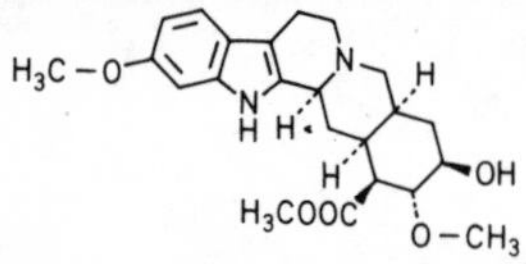	R	R	10	—	51

Sugars and Sugar Derivatives

No.	Compound	Obs.	Pred.	Optical Yield %	Chemical Yield %	Ref.
41	5-deoxy-5-ethylthio-1,2-O-isopropylidene-D-xylofuranose 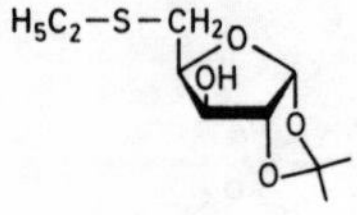	S	R	25	81	26
		S	R	26	73	26

| 42 | 5-O-ethyl-1,2-O-isopropylidene-D-xylofuranose 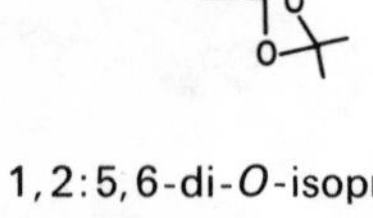 | S | R | 28 | 77 | 26 |
| | | S | R | 28 | 70 | 26 |

| 43 | 1,2:5,6-di-O-isopropylidene-D-glucofuranose 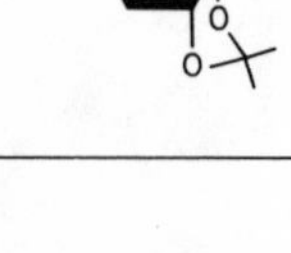 | S | R | 34 | 79 | 26 |
| | | S | R | 33 | 77 | 26 |

Table 6. (continued)

No.	Compound	Conf.[a] Obs.	Pred.	Optical Yield %	Chemical Yield %	Ref.
	Alcohol ROH			Atrolactic Acid		
44	1,2:5,6-di-*O*-cyclohexylidene-D-glucofuranose	*S*	*R*	38	72	[26]
		S	*R*	37	68	[26]
45	1,2-*O*-cyclohexylidene-5-*O*-trityl-D-xylofuranose 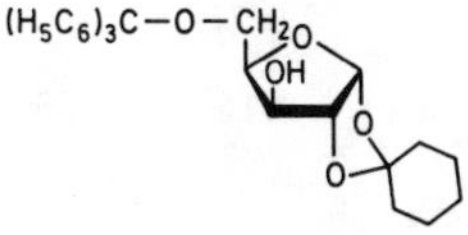	*S*	*S*	53	68	[52]
46	1,2-*O*-cyclohexylidene-5-*O*-trityl-D-xylofuranose on polymer 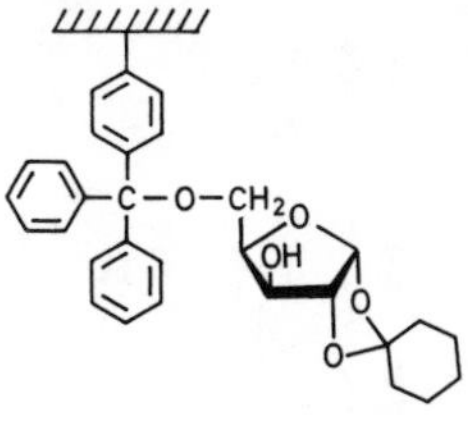	*S*	*S*	65	77	[52]

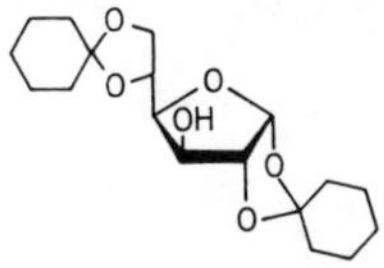

Miscellaneous

No.	Compound	Conf.[a] Obs.	Pred.	Optical Yield %	Chemical Yield %	Ref.
47	(−)-epi-afzelechin trimethyl ether 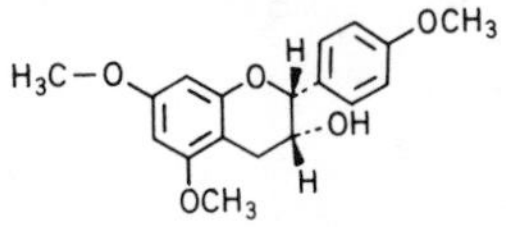	*R*	*R*	—	—	[28]
48	(−)-epicatechin-tetramethyl ether 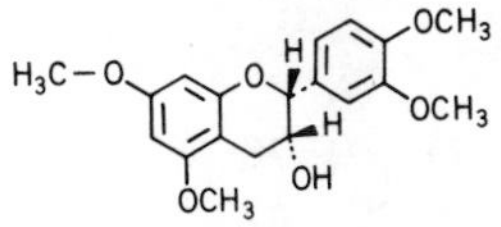	*R*[e]	*R*	—	—	[28]
49	(+)-catechin-5,7:3′,4′-tetramethyl ether 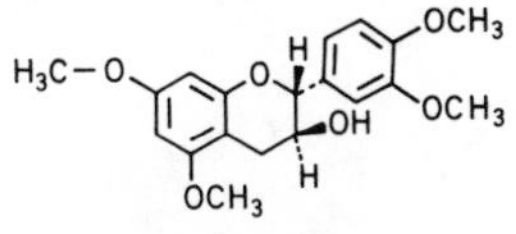	*S*[e]	*R*	3[f]	60	[28]

Table 6. (continued)

	Alcohol ROH			Atrolactic Acid		
No.	Compound	Conf.[a] Obs.	Pred.	Optical Yield %	Chemical Yield %	Ref.

| 50 | methyl tetrahydrogibberellate | S^d | S | 10 | 71 | [32] |

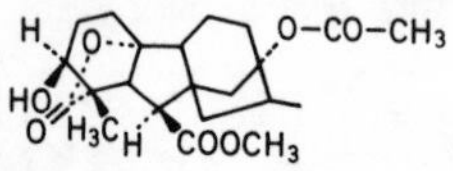

Biphenyls and Binaphthyls

| 51 | (+)-1-(1-naphthyl)-2-naphthol | R^g | R | 85 | 41 | [33] |

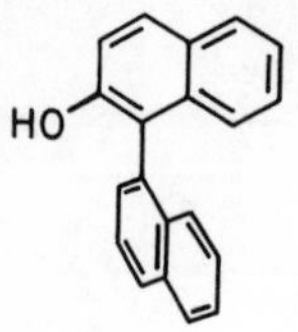

24

| 52 | 4β-Hydroxy-4,5-dihydro-3H-cyclohepta-[2,1-a:1′,2′-c]dinaphthalene | R^g | R | 20 | — | [34] |

| 53 | (+)-phenyldihydrothebaine bismethine | R^g | R | 93 | 61 | [33] |

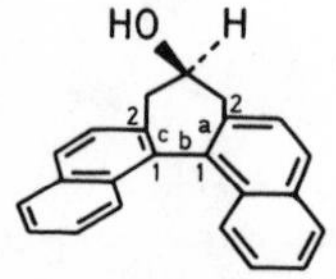

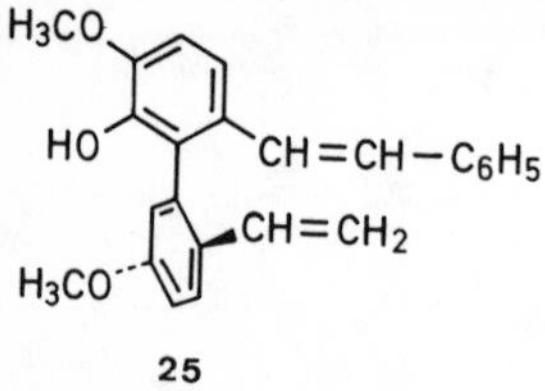

25

| 54 | (+)-phenyldihydrothebaine | R^g | R | 71 | 78 | [33] |
| | | R | R | 70 | 67 | [33] |

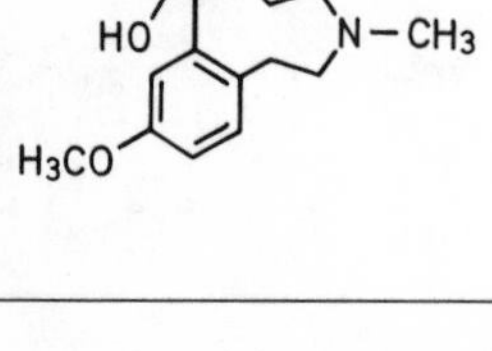

Table 6. (continued)

No.	Compound	Conf.[a] Obs.	Conf.[a] Pred.	Optical Yield %	Chemical Yield %	Ref.
	Alcohol ROH			Atrolactic Acid		
55	(+)-phenyldihydrothebaine isomethine	R^g	R	91	70	33
56	(+)-phenyldihydrothebaine dihydroisomethine	R^g	R	89	63	33

For No. 55:

H_3CO, HO, H_3CO ... CH_2-CH-N with C_6H_5, CH_3, $CH=CH_2$, CH_3

For No. 56:

H_3CO, HO, H_3CO ... CH_2-CH-N with C_6H_5, CH_3, CH_2-CH_3, CH_3

[a] Configuration of the asymmetric carbon atom carrying the hydroxy group.
[b] The configuration of this alcohol has been assigned primarily upon the basis of the atrolactic acid asymmetric synthesis, and has since been confirmed.
[c] The configuration of pinacolyl alcohol has been confirmed by chemical correlation[53].
[d] The configuration of this alcohol has been assigned only by the atrolactic acid method.
[e] This is the correct configuration.
[f] See text p. 29.
[g] Configuration of the biphenyl portion according to the revised rules of Cahn, Ingold and Prelog[11].
[h] In brackets is given the year of publication cited in the respective reference.

5. Other Asymmetric Syntheses Starting from a-Keto Esters Determination of the Absolute Configuration of a-Hydroxy Acids

The Prelog rule, as exemplified by the atrolactic acid synthesis, has been used primarily for the determination of absolute configuration of secondary alcohols. In principle, however, it should be applicable to asymmetric syntheses involving the reaction of any Grignard reagent with any optically active a-keto ester of known configuration (relative to the alcohol employed), and this has been verified in practice. Reactions of this type, in which an a-keto ester of an alcohol of known configuration is treated with a Grignard reagent, have been utilized for the determination of absolute configuration not of alcohols, but of a-hydroxy acids. More often than not in such investigations, the a-hydroxy acid obtained at the end of the sequence has not been resolved, and hence the extent of the asymmetric synthesis is unknown. If the a-hydroxy acid has been resolved,

[41] W. Acklin and V. Prelog, Helv. Chim. Acta 42, 1239 (1959).
[42] T. Irie, M. Suzuki, and T. Masamune, Tetrahedron 24, 4193 (1968).
[43] M. J. Kubitsceck and W. A. Bonner, J. Org. Chem. 26, 2194 (1961).
[44] V. Prelog, O. Ceder, and M. Wilhelm, Helv. Chim. Acta 38, 303 (1955).

however, then the absolute configuration can be deduced from an asymmetric synthesis carried out with an optically active *a*-keto ester of known configuration. In cases where the acids in question have never been resolved, it is impossible to know whether or not the optical purity of the product is significant as a result of the synthesis; apart from this exception, however, prediction of absolute configuration by the Prelog rule can be made.

For example, treatment of the (–)-menthyl ester of pyruvic acid with ethylmagnesium iodide gives dextrorotatory 2-hydroxy-2-methylbutanoic acid. Application of the Prelog rule indicates that this acid should have the *S* configuration, and it has been shown by chemical correlation that the corresponding enantiomer, (–)-2-hydroxy-2-methylbutanoic acid, has in fact the *R* configuration[54].

Similarly, treatment of (–)-menthyl pyruvate with ethynylmagnesium bromide gives (+)-2-hydroxy-2-methylbut-3-ynoic acid[55] which, according to the Prelog rule, should be *S*. This prediction has been confirmed by chemical correlation of the product with 2-hydroxy-2-methylbutanoic acid.

Details of further examples of this type of synthesis are listed in Tables 7–9.

Table 7:

34   35

R	R'	configuration	$[a]^{(0)}$	e.e. (%)	yield (%)	Ref.
CH₃	C₂H₅	S	+	–		4 (1906)d
CH₃	HC≡C–	S	–6.5	–	33	56
CH₃	‖	S	+0.7	2	25	55
‖	‖	S	+0.3	1	15	55
‖	C(CH₃)₃	S	+0.9	–	–	57
‖	C₆H₅	S	–	14	78	4 (1906)d
‖	‖	S	–	18	50	58
‖	4-tolyl	S	–	13	–	8
‖	4-anisyl	S	–	15	30	7 (1932)d
C₂H₅	C₆H₅	S	–	28	30	59, 60, 61
‖	i-C₆H₁₃	Sᵇ	+1.1	–	63	60, 61
i-C₆H₁₃	C₂H₅	Rᵇ	–0.6	–	87	60, 61
C₆H₅	C₂H₅	Rᵇ	–	35	38	59
‖	HC≡C–	R	–	32	17	56
‖	4-tolyl	Sᵇ	–	15	63	8
4-anisyl	CH₃	R	–	26	65	7 (1932)d
1-naphthyl	CH₃	Rᵇ	+10.0	29ᵃ	68	7, (231, 412, 1931)e
‖	C₂H₅	Rᵇ	+ 6.8	–	70	
‖	C₆H₅	Rᵇ	–12.7	–	20	

ᵃ this is an estimation; 1-naphtylmandelic acid has not been completely resolved.   ᵇ, ᵈ, ᵉ see Table 9

Table 8:

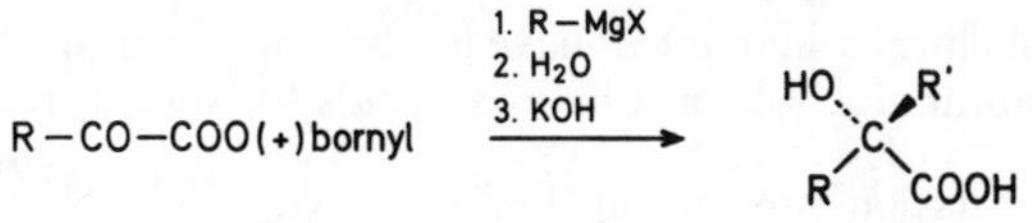

$$R-CO-COO(+)bornyl \quad \xrightarrow[\text{3. KOH}]{\begin{array}{l}\text{1. R–MgX}\\\text{2. } H_2O\end{array}} \quad \underset{R}{\overset{HO}{\diagdown}}\underset{\diagup}{\overset{\diagup}{C}}\underset{COOH}{\overset{R'}{}}$$

36 a   **37**

R	R'	configuration	$[a]_D^{(0)}$	e.e. (%)	yield (%)	Ref.
CH_3	$HC \equiv C-$	R^b	+6.6	–	24	[56]
C_6H_5	$CH_2-CH(CH_3)_2$	S^b	+2.5	–	67	[2]
C_6H_5	1-naphthyl	R^b	+1.0	–	66	[2]

Table 9:

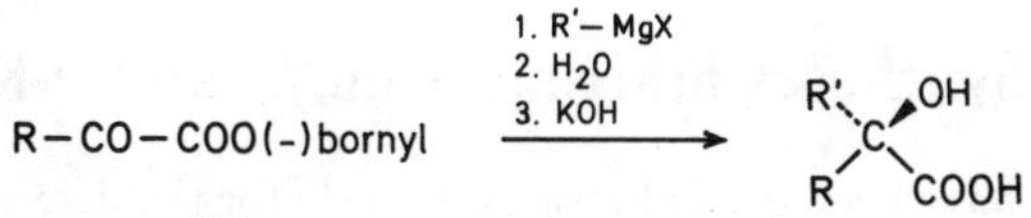

$$R-CO-COO(-)bornyl \quad \xrightarrow[\text{3. KOH}]{\begin{array}{l}\text{1. R'– MgX}\\\text{2. } H_2O\end{array}} \quad \underset{R}{\overset{R'}{\diagdown}}\underset{\diagup}{\overset{\diagup}{C}}\underset{COOH}{\overset{OH}{}}$$

36 b   **37**

R	R'	configuration	$[a]_D^{(0)}$	e.e. (%)	yield (%)	Ref.
C_6H_5	C_2H_5	R	–	12	57	[4 (1906)d]
C_6H_5	$CH_2-CH(CH_3)_2$	R	+1.0	–	45	[8]
C_6H_5	4-tolyl	S	–	7	–	[4 (1906)d]
1-naphthyl	CH_3	R	–3.5	–	95	[7 (231, 412, 1931)e]

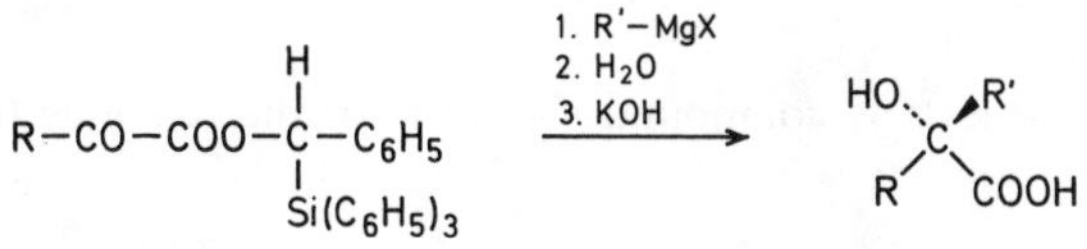

$$R-CO-COO-\underset{\underset{Si(C_6H_5)_3}{|}}{\overset{\overset{H}{|}}{C}}-C_6H_5 \quad \xrightarrow[\text{3. KOH}]{\begin{array}{l}\text{1. R'– MgX}\\\text{2. } H_2O\end{array}} \quad \underset{R}{\overset{HO}{\diagdown}}\underset{\diagup}{\overset{\diagup}{C}}\underset{COOH}{\overset{R'}{}}$$

38   **37**

$R = C_6H_5$, $R' = CH_3$ config.: $S^{c\,62}$
enantiomeric excess: 28 %
yield: 93 %

[b] The configuration of this 1-hydroxy acid has been assigned primarily upon the basis of Prelog's rule.

[c] The configuration of the phenyl-triphenylsilyl-carbinol has been assigned upon the basis of Prelog's rule; this assignment has been confirmed by X-ray crystallography[63].

[d] In brackets is given the year of publication cited in the respective reference.

[e] The brackets include volume number, page number and year of publication cited in the respective reference.

[45] W.G. Dauben, D.F. Dickel, O. Jeger, and V. Prelog, Helv. Chim. Acta **36**, 325 (1953).

[46] V. Prelog and G. Tsatsas, Helv. Chim. Acta **36**, 1178 (1953).

[47] J.C. Danilewicz, D.C.F. Garbutt, A. Horeau, and W. Klyne, J. Chem. Soc. **1964**, 2254.

[48] K. Tsuda and R. Hayatsu, Chem. Pharm. Bull. (Tokyo) **6**, 580 (1958).

6. Reduction of α-Keto Esters

Asymmetric reductions of chiral α-keto esters have not been used for the determination of absolute configuration of either chiral alcohols or α-hydroxy acids for several reasons:

(i)   Observed asymmetric inductions are normally low[1].
(ii) In reductions carried out under heterogeneous conditions, the configuration of the acid which is obtained may sometimes depend on the pH of the medium. Thus, catalytic hydrogenation of (–)-menthyl phenyl-glyoxylate over palladium sometimes (usually basic media) gives *(R)*-mandelic acid and at other times *(S)*-mandelic acid[64].
(iii) The mandelate esters obtained by reduction of phenylglyoxylate esters are difficult to hydrolyze without concomitant racemization. This difficulty can, however, be circumvented either by subjecting the corresponding mandelate *O*-acetate to hydrolysis or, better, by reduction of the mandelic ester to the corresponding diol with lithium aluminum hydride.
(iv) It has been claimed[65] that the ester carbonyl group in phenylglyoxylate esters is more easily reduced than the ketonic carbonyl group. The validity of this claim – which, if correct, would prejudice accurate prediction of the steric course of reaction – has, however, been questioned[1, 66].

7. Asymmetric Syntheses Starting from β- and γ-Keto Esters

Phenylglyoxylate esters have been used almost exclusively for the determination of absolute configuration by the Prelog rule, and little effort has been expended on the use of other keto esters. β-Keto esters in which there is a hydrogen atom alpha to the ketonic carbonyl group are of little utility as treatment with Grignard reagents does not result in addition to the carbonyl group, but merely in enolization. γ-Keto esters have been used successfully: for example, addition of methylmagnesium bromide to (–)-menthyl 3-benzoylpropanoate (**39**) gives, after the standard reaction sequence, (–)-4-hydroxy-4-phenylpentanoic acid, with an optical purity of 10–17%[58].

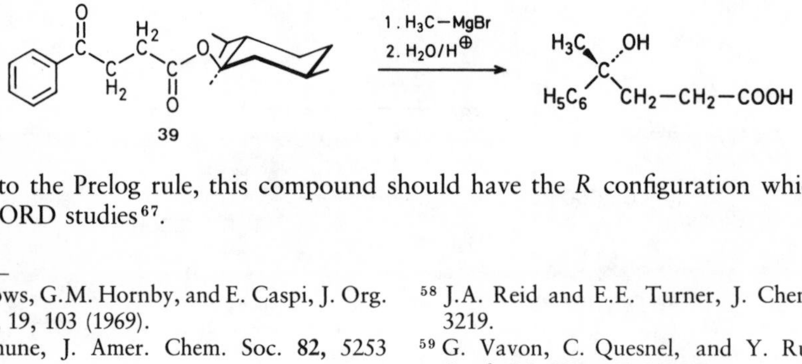

39

According to the Prelog rule, this compound should have the R configuration which has been verified by ORD studies[67].

[49] E.P. Burrows, G.M. Hornby, and E. Caspi, J. Org. Chem. **34**, 19, 103 (1969).
[50] S. Masamune, J. Amer. Chem. Soc. **82**, 5253 (1960).
[51] Y. Ban and O. Yonemitsu, Chem. and Ind. **1961**, 948.
[52] M. Kawana and S. Emoto, Tetrahedron Lett. **48**, 4855 (1972).
[53] J. Jacobus, Z. Majerski, K. Mislow, and P. von Rague Schleyer, J. Amer. Chem. Soc. **91**, 1998 (1969).
[54] B.W. Christensen and A. Kjaer, Acta Chem. Scand. **16**, 2466 (1962).
[55] D. Dugat, M. Verny, and R. Vessière, Tetrahedron Lett. **27**, 1715 (1971).
[56] I. Iwai and Y. Yura, C.A. **55**, 3646 (1961).
[57] R.J.D. Evans and S.R. Landor, Proc. Chem. Soc. **1962**, 182.
[58] J.A. Reid and E.E. Turner, J. Chem. Soc. **1951**, 3219.
[59] G. Vavon, C. Quesnel, and Y. Runavot, C.R. Acad. Sci. **237**, 617 (1953).
[60] V. Prelog and E. Watanabe, Justus Liebigs Ann. Chem. **603**, 1 (1957).
[61] R.H. Cornforth, J.W. Cornforth, and V. Prelog, Justus Liebigs Ann. Chem. **634**, 197 (1960).
[62] M. Biernbaum and H.S. Mosher, Tetrahedron Lett. **1968**, 5789.
[63] K.T. Black and H. Hope, J. Amer. Chem. Soc. **93**, 3053 (1971).
[64] S. Mitsui and Y. Imai, C.A. **67**, 43934 (1967).
[65] J.A. Berson and M.A. Greenbaum, J. Amer. Chem. Soc. **81**, 6456 (1959).
[66] J. Canceill and J. Jacques, Bull. Soc. Chim. France **1970**, 2180.
[67] L. Verbit, S. Mitsui, and Y. Senda, Tetrahedron **22**, 753 (1966).

Nevertheless, the paucity of information available on the reactions of keto esters other than phenylglyoxylates, and the low optical yields that have been reported in specific cases, mean that the Prelog rule cannot be unambiguously applied in such instances for the prediction of configuration.

8.   Conclusions

Under the conditions of application defined by Prelog, the empirical rule does allow prediction to be made of the steric course of an asymmetric synthesis carried out with a chiral α-keto ester, and the predictions have been confirmed in the majority of cases studied. The method has been widely used for the determination of absolute configuration in compounds where no prior information was available; in this way, the absolute configurations of both secondary alcohols and hydroxy carboxylic acids have been determined. There are no known exceptions to the rule. This latter point, together with the development of modern experimental techniques (NMR shift reagents, GLC of diastereomeric derivatives), do show that Prelog's method remains both a sure and sensitive tool for the determination of the absolute configuration of secondary alcohols.

Determination of the Configuration of Secondary Alcohols by Partial Resolution

A. Horeau

Collège de France, Paris

Table of Contents

1.   General Discussion

1.1.   Principles of the Method

The properties of two enantiomers (antipodes) are exactly the same with respect to reaction with an achiral substrate. Thus, for example, if the rate of reaction of one enantiomer B_d with an achiral substance S under certain conditions is v_1, the rate of reaction of the antipode B_l with the same substrate under the same conditions will also be v_1 (Scheme 1a). This identity in properties is not,

$$
a \begin{cases} B_d & + & S & \xrightarrow{v_1} & \text{products} \\ B_l & + & S & \xrightarrow{v_1} & \text{products} \end{cases}
$$

$$
b \begin{cases} B_d & + & A^* & \xrightarrow{v_2} & \text{products} \\ B_l & + & A^* & \xrightarrow{v_3} & \text{products} \end{cases}
$$

$$
c \begin{cases} B_d & + & A^{\circ} & \xrightarrow{v_3} & \text{products} \\ B_l & + & A^{\circ} & \xrightarrow{v_2} & \text{products} \end{cases} \qquad \text{Scheme 1}
$$

however, valid with respect to reaction with a chiral substrate A. Consider, for example, the reactions of the two B enantiomers with an enantiomer A^*: the rates of reaction of B_d and B_l with A^* may not be identical, and B_d may react faster than B_l (Scheme 1b, $v_2 > v_3$). Assuming $v_2 > v_3$, it follows that treatment of A^* with an excess of *racemic* B (i.e. where B_d and B_l are present in equal amounts) will result in the enantiomer B_l being present in excess over B_d at the end of the reaction. This can readily be confirmed by isolation of residual B_l from the reaction mixture and determination of the rotatory power; in the example given the material thus obtained will be laevorotatory.

A specific example of this procedure is the reaction between an optically active alcohol A^*OH and a *racemic* carboxylic acid $Q_d-COOH + Q_l-COOH$ (as the anhydride or acid chloride), and the following statement illustrates such esterifications[1, 2]: treatment of a pyridine solution of (−)-menthol with excess of racemic 2-phenylbutanoic anhydride

$$
\left(\begin{array}{c} H_5C_6-CH-CO \\ | \\ C_2H_5 \end{array} \right)_2 O
$$

will give, after hydrolysis of excess anhydride at the end of the reaction, extraction of the resulting acid with base, and acidification of the basic extract, an acid which shows a discrete optical rotation. This general approach is obviously valid for both of the enantiomers of A. Thus, with respect to the above general case, if the antipode A° is used instead of A^* then the rates of reaction of this enantiomer with B_d and B_l will now be v_3 and v_2 respectively (Scheme 1c). Consequently, treatment of $A^{\circ}-OH$ with excess racemic Q−COOH will again result in production of an optically active acid, but the sign of rotation will be opposite to that of the acid obtained when A^*-OH is used.

It is therefore evident that *the sign of the acid which is isolated depends on the absolute configuration of the antipode of A−OH which is used in the reaction.* Consequently, the question arises: is it possible to establish a relationship between the sign of the 2-phenylbutanoic acid which is isolated from the reaction mixture and the absolute configuration of the alcohol involved in the esterifica-

---

A^* refers to one enantiomer, the antipode of which is A°, and does not refer to rotatory power.

[1] A. Horeau, Tetrahedron Lett. **1961**, 506.
[2] A. Horeau, Tetrahedron Lett. **1962**, 965.

[3] A. Horeau and H.B. Kagan, Tetrahedron **20**, 2431 (1964).

tion? The possibility that such a relationship did exist constituted the basis of the investigation from which the Horeau method of "partial resolution" or of "kinetic resolution" developed [1-5]. Several variations have been adopted in the experimental verification of this relationship, and these are discussed later [6-10].

The partial resolution method has been employed in most cases, and the procedure which is always involved consists of esterification of a chiral secondary alcohol with the anhydride of 2-phenylbutyric acid in pyridine solution. The overall process remains empirical in nature, as little is known of the transition states involved in the individual reactions. The validity of the method is based on the fact that in all cases which have been investigated with secondary alcohols of known configuration, agreement between prediction and experimental result is perfect; hence, the method can be applied with confidence to other alcohols, the configuration of which is not known.

The procedure can be used when only very small quantities of materials are available, for example 10^{-4} mol, and the major experimental limitation is simply the precision with which the optical rotation of the isolated acid can be determined. Moreover, the method is simple and rapid from a manipulative point of view: the acid left in excess at the end of the reaction can be isolated and separated from neutral materials simply by hydrolysis of the excess anhydride and extraction with base.

An experimental modification of the procedure is described later (see p. 82) which eliminates the necessity of polarimetric measurements on the residual acid, and use of this technique allows the operation to be carried out with very small quantities of reagents (down to $\sim 1\,mg$) [10].

1.2. Kinetic Origin of Resolution

The method outlined above involves *kinetic resolution;* it is not an equilibrium process, nor are retro-condensations involved. These conclusions are confirmed by the observation that pure (−)-menthyl (+) or (−)-2-phenylbutanoate can be dissolved in either hot or cold pyridine and then reisolated completely unchanged [11].

Furthermore, the rate of reaction of (−)-menthol with optically pure laevorotatory 2-phenylbutanoic anhydride in benzene/pyridine has been measured. Benzene is employed as a co-solvent in order to slow down the reaction and thus to facilitate the rate measurements, which are carried out polarimetrically. The molecular rotation of the mixture of products formed is different from that of (−)-menthol, and it is possible to define a half reaction time. Repetition of the same procedure using the dextrorotatory anhydride reveals that the half reaction time in this case is about three times greater than that of the laevorotatory anhydride. Consequently, it follows that reaction of (−)-menthol with an excess of *racemic* 2-phenylbutanoic anhydride in pyridine solution will result in a predominance of the dextrorotatory acid after hydrolysis. The optical yield, which in this case is about 50% and which will be defined later, can be deduced from the ratio of the observed rates [11].

1.3. Rules for the Prediction of Absolute Configuration

It has been found experimentally that there is a relationship between the sign of the isolated 2-phenylbutyric acid and the absolute configuration of the alcohol used in the reaction. This relationship is defined as follows:

[4] A. Horeau and A. Nouaille, Tetrahedron Lett. **1966**, 3953.

[5] A. Marquet and A. Horeau, Bull. Soc. Chim. France **1967**, 124.

[6] A. Horeau, J. Amer. Chem. Soc. 86, 3171 (1964).

[7] A. Horeau, Bull. Soc. Chim. France **1964**, 2673.

[8] R. Weidmann and A. Horeau, Bull. Soc. Chim. France **1967**, 117.

[9] A. Horeau and A. Nouaille, Tetrahedron Lett. **1971**, 1939.

[10] R. Weidmann and A. Horeau, Tetrahedron Lett. **1973**, 2979.

[11] A. Horeau, unpubl. results.

If the 2-phenylbutanoic acid which is isolated is laevorotatory, the secondary alcohol will be that in which, in a Fischer projection, the hydroxy group is down, the hydrogen atom up, and the larger of the two remaining substituent groups is on the right.

If the acid which is isolated is dextrorotatory, the secondary alcohol will be that in which, in a Fischer projection (i.e. where the hydroxy group is down and the hydrogen atom up), the larger of the two remaining substituent groups is on the left (the above two statements are obviously

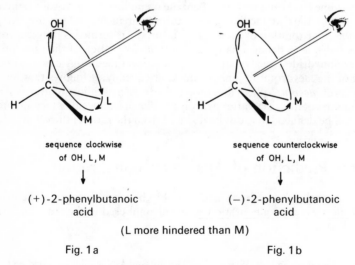

complementary). Alternatively, the configuration of the alcohol can be predicted in the following terms:

If the acid which is isolated is dextrorotatory, the secondary alcohol will be that in which the larger of the two remaining substituent groups is on the right hand side of the molecule when it is viewed as shown in Fig. 1a.

In certain publications describing applications of the Horeau method, the definition of absolute configuration of the secondary alcohol being studied has been changed from that illustrated in Fig. 1 to use of the R or S nomenclature for the chiral center, according to the rules formulated by Cahn, Ingold and Prelog[12]. This substitution of R and S for the pictorial representation shown in Fig. 1 should be avoided at all costs, because implicit in this use of the Cahn-Ingold-Prelog nomenclature is the assumption that the L, or "more bulky" group, takes precedence over the M, or "less bulky" group. The concepts used by Cahn, Ingold and Prelog, however, are by no means rigorous for the classification of the size of various groups. It is impossible to predict which of the two alcohol antipodes in Fig. 1 should be defined by the letter R (or S). It is certainly true that there are very many cases in which L has priority over M, but it is equally true that there is a smaller number of cases where the reverse situation is found. In 2-propanol-1-d_3, for instance, the CD_3 group is less bulky than the CH_3 group[4, 13] but according to the Cahn-Ingold-Prelog rules, CD_3 takes priority over CH_3.

The a or β, cis or trans, threo or erythyro nature of a hydroxy group in a molecule bearing several asymmetric carbon atoms:
The method which is described below can be utilized for the determination of the absolute configuration of, for example, a 2-alkylcycloalkanols 2, where the trans relationship of the OH and R groups has been established. Conversely, if the absolute configuration of the corresponding ketone 1 is known, it is possible to use the method for the determination of the cis or trans nature of the

$$
\underset{\textbf{1}}{\text{O=C–C(R)(H), (CH}_2)_n} \longrightarrow \underset{\textbf{2}}{\text{HO–C(H)–C(R)(H), (CH}_2)_n}
$$

two epimeric alcohols formed on reduction of the ketone. This procedure has been employed for the determination of the a or β character of a secondary hydroxy group mainly in the area of natural products such as steroids (see Ref.[3]).

1.4. Material Balance in Kinetic Resolution

Consider the overall material balance for an esterification involving one equivalent of alcohol and two equivalents of acid, and which is assumed to be stereospecific. From the point of view of simplicity consider first the acid itself as reagent rather than the anhydride; this leads to Eq. (1):

$$ A_d\text{–OH} + Q_d\text{–COOH} + Q_l\text{–COOH} \longrightarrow Q_d\text{–COOA}_d + Q_l\text{–COOH} \qquad (1) $$

Such esterifications are never, however, stereospecific, but only partially selective. If a is the fraction of the dextrorotatory alcohol which reacts with the acid to form the ester, then Eq. (1) can be modified to Eq. (2):

$$ A_d\text{–OH} + Q_d\text{–COOH} + Q_l\text{–COOH} \quad \Bigg\{ \begin{array}{l} \text{esters}: \quad \begin{array}{l} a\ Q_d\text{–COOA}_d \\ (1-a)\ Q_l\text{–COOA}_d \end{array} \\[1em] \text{acids}: \quad \begin{array}{l} a\ Q_l\text{–COOH} \\ (1-a)\ Q_d\text{–COOH} \end{array} \end{array} \qquad (2) $$

The overall material balance for the general case of partial resolution is given in Eqs. (3a) and (3b). These equations have been constructed to conform with the experimental situation; i.e. the anhydrides are used, the threo form in Eq. (3a) and the meso form in Eq. (3b) and the reaction is

[12] R.S. Cahn, C. Ingold, and V. Prelog, Angew. Chem. Int. Ed. 5, 385 (1966).

[13] A. Horeau, A. Nouaille, and K. Mislow, J. Amer. Chem. Soc. 87, 4957 (1965).

performed between n equivalents of the alcohol and an excess of N equivalents of 2-phenylbutanoic anhydride.

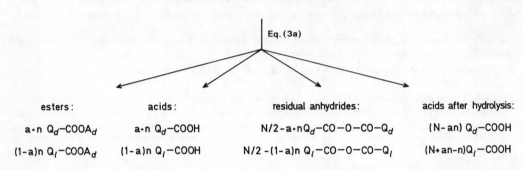

$$n \cdot A_d-OH \quad + \quad N(1/2\ Q_d-CO-O-CO-Q_d \quad + \quad 1/2\ Q_l-CO-O-CO-Q_l)$$

threo anhydride

Eq. (3a)

esters:	acids:	residual anhydrides:	acids after hydrolysis:
$a \cdot n\ Q_d-COOA_d$	$a \cdot n\ Q_d-COOH$	$N/2-a \cdot nQ_d-CO-O-CO-Q_d$	$(N-an)\ Q_d-COOH$
$(1-a)n\ Q_l-COOA_d$	$(1-a)n\ Q_l-COOH$	$N/2-(1-a)n\ Q_l-CO-O-CO-Q_l$	$(N+an-n)Q_l-COOH$

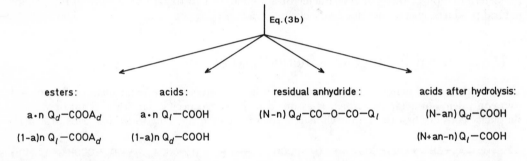

$$n\ A_d-OH \quad + \quad N \cdot Q_d-CO-O-CO-Q_l$$

meso anhydride

Eq. (3b)

esters:	acids:	residual anhydride:	acids after hydrolysis:
$a \cdot n\ Q_d-COOA_d$	$a \cdot n\ Q_l-COOH$	$(N-n)\ Q_d-CO-O-CO-Q_l$	$(N-an)\ Q_d-COOH$
$(1-a)n\ Q_l-COOA_d$	$(1-a)n\ Q_d-COOH$		$(N+an-n)\ Q_l-COOH$

The relative amounts of dextro- and laevorotatory acids after hydrolysis are the same in both cases, and when $a > 0.5$, the laevorotatory acid is obtained in excess $(N+an-n > N-an)$. The optical purity of the isolated acid is given by

$$\frac{(N+an-n)-(N-an)}{(N+an-n)+(N-an)} = (2a-1)\frac{n}{2N-n}$$

The yield r in the esterification step and the number of equivalents $n'(n' = nr)$ of the chiral alcohol which have effectively been esterified can be determined at the end of the reaction and after the hydrolysis step by titration with acid. It is this number n' which should be considered.

If the 2-phenylbutanoic acid isolated after the partial resolution is laevorotatory (i.e. Q_l-COOH in excess over Q_d-COOH), it follows that the ester Q_d-COOA_d will be obtained in excess over Q_l-COOA_d. These esters can often be differentiated by the use of GLC or NMR; if it can be shown that the two esters are indeed present in different amounts, then there has been a "partial resolution". Experimentally, this is normally done by identifying the signals or peaks due to the major component with one of the esters which has been prepared independently by treatment of the alcohol A_d-OH with either dextro or laevorotatory 2-phenylbutanoic anhydride of high optical purity.

The above results for esters can be related to those described previously for cases where an optically active acid is isolated, and a similar general rule can be formulated: *when the ester Q_d-COOA_d*

is obtained in excess over the ester Q_l–COOA$_d$, *the* A$_d$–OH *alcohol will have the configuration shown in* 3.

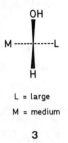

L = large
M = medium

3

Using the technique, it is possible to work with the *racemic alcohol* (A$_d$–OH + A$_l$–OH) and the *racemic anhydride* (see p. 68). If the ester Q_d–COOA$_d$, Q_l–COOA$_l$ is formed in excess over the ester Q_l–COOA$_d$, Q_d–COOA$_l$, then the configuration of the A$_d$–OH alcohol is defined as shown in 3.

This procedure, which has been developed recently, is less general than the classical method since it implies a distinction between two diastereoisomers of closely related structure. Use of this method can be advantageous in certain cases, however, as it can be employed with very small quantities of alcohol[10].

1.5. Optical Yield

Preferential esterification of a chiral alcohol by one of the diastereoisomers of *racemic* 2-phenylbutanoic acid can be highly stereoselective in certain cases, but never stereospecific. An important concept in this respect is the optical yield. The *optical yield* is the ratio between the optical purity of the 2-phenylbutanoic acid which is isolated from the reaction, and which is measured experimentally, and the optical purity which would have been realized had the reaction proceeded with complete stereospecificity. In this case, the rotatory power should be equal to the rotatory power of optically pure 2-phenylbutanoic acid (96.8°) multiplied by the ratio n/2N-n which is derived from Eqs.(3a) and (3b) when a = 1. Under normal circumstances, reactions are carried out with one equivalent of the alcohol and two equivalents of 2-phenylbutanoic anhydride. If esterification proceeds to completion, n = 1 and N = 2, and the optical purity in a stereospecific reaction will be ⅓; if the 2-phenylbutanoic acid were isolated and its rotation measured, it would be found to be 32.3°.

Sometimes, the determination of the absolute configuration has to be carried out with compounds which are not optically pure, as is often the case, for example, with the products obtained from asymmetric syntheses. When the optical purity is not known, a minimum value for the optical yield can be obtained by carrying out the calculation in the usual manner and as if the compound were optically pure. When the optical purity is known, the true optical yield can be obtained by dividing the apparent optical yield (calculated on the basis that the compound was optically pure) by the optical purity and expressing the resultant value as a percentage.

The value of the optical yield is often of considerable interest, and hence it is desirable that it should be determined in a rigorous manner. Exact determinations are essential in cases where the method is extended to calculation of rotatory powers by double resolution[6, 7]. Where the objective of the method is, initially, the determination of absolute configuration, however, establishment of the sign of the 2-phenylbutanoic acid in an unambiguous manner is the more important process.

Consequently, values of optical yields quoted in the literature should be considered as accurate only to within about 20% (unless otherwise specified). The major reasons for this degree of error are racemization of the acid in the presence of the anhydride or inexact estimation of the extent of esterification.

It is often possible, in an apparently paradoxical fashion, to attain a much more precise value for the optical yield by using (under very simple conditions) the racemic form of both the alcohol in question and the anhydride[10]. This can be demonstrated as follows: using the alcohol A_l–OH, Eq. (3b), for example, changes to (3b'):

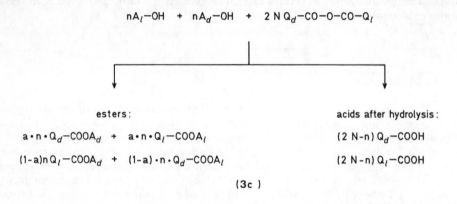

$$n\ A_l\text{–OH}\ +\ N\cdot Q_d\text{–CO–O–CO–}Q_l$$

esters:

$$a\cdot n\cdot Q_l\text{–COO}A_l$$

$$(1\text{-}a)n\ Q_d\text{–COO}A_l$$

acids after hydrolysis:

$$(N\text{-}an)\ Q_l\text{–COOH}$$

$$(N\text{-}an\text{-}n)\ Q_d\text{–COOH}$$

(3b')

That is, the optical yield is the same, but the sign of the acid which is isolated is obviously opposite, since the configuration of the alcohol being examined is inverted (see Scheme 1b and 1c). The value of the optical yield "2a–1" is given not only by the rotatory power of the isolated acid, but also by comparison of the relative quantities of the diastereoisomeric esters.

Consider now the situation when the reaction occurs between the *racemic* alcohol and the *racemic* anhydride; Eq. (3c) can be deduced from Eqs. (3b) and (3b'):

$$nA_l\text{–OH}\ +\ nA_d\text{–OH}\ +\ 2\,N\,Q_d\text{–CO–O–CO–}Q_l$$

esters:

$$a\cdot n\cdot Q_d\text{–COO}A_d\ +\ a\cdot n\cdot Q_l\text{–COO}A_l$$

$$(1\text{-}a)n\,Q_l\text{–COO}A_d\ +\ (1\text{-}a)\cdot n\cdot Q_d\text{–COO}A_l$$

acids after hydrolysis:

$$(2\,N\text{-}n)\,Q_d\text{–COOH}$$

$$(2\,N\text{-}n)\,Q_l\text{–COOH}$$

(3c)

Obviously, the acid which is isolated is *racemic*. It should be noted, however, that the two antipodes Q_d–COOA_d and Q_l–COOA_l, the total amount of which is 2 an, have the same chemical and spectral properties. A similar situation exists with respect to the pair Q_l–COOA_d and Q_d–COOA_l, the total amount of which is 2(1–a). Consequently, if it is possible to evaluate the ratio a/1–a of these two pairs of diastereoisomeric antipodes, the optical yield "2a–1" can readily be calculated [the rationale behind this approach can similarly be applied to the *threo* anhydride in (3a)]. It should be noted that the value of a is the same in Eq. (3c) as in the previously established Eqs. (3a), (3b) or (3b'). However, this is apparently true for the latter equations, only when N is much greater than n (justification of this approximation: see p. 63).

It is remarkable also that the ratio a/1–a of the *racemic* diastereoisomers is independent of the quantities n and N involved in the reaction, and therefore of the extent of esterification.

1.6.   Properties of 2-Phenylbutanoic Acid and Anhydrides

As almost all of the work carried out on partial resolution has involved the use of 2-phenylbutanoic anhydride, it is convenient and useful to give here a brief outline of the main properties of this anhydride and of the corresponding acid, as these have a bearing on the manner in which the method is employed. More complete details are given in the experimental section.

racemic 2-Phenylbutanoic acid is a solid, mp 41°C, while each of the antipodes is a liquid; resolution of the racemic acid can be effected in a number of ways, for example by the use of a chiral base such as cinchonidine[14] or either of the antipodes of 2-phenylethylamine[15]. The rotation of the optically pure acid is $[a]_D^{22} = 96.8°$ (neat, $l = 1$); the value varies considerably with temperature, and the following figures are illustrative (the data refer to the liquid state, the sodium D line, and $l = 1$):

$$[a]^{15} = 100.1° \qquad [a]^{17} = 99.06° \qquad [a]^{19} = 98.16°$$
$$[a]^{21} = 97.24° \qquad [a]^{23} = 96.26° \qquad [a]^{25} = 95.36°$$

and indicate a variation of about one degree in rotation for every two degrees of temperature. The density of the liquid varies only from $d^{15} = 1.067$ to $d^{25} = 1.061$.
The rotatory dispersion is illustrated by the following rotations:

$$[a]_D^{22.5} = 96.6° \qquad [a]_{578}^{22.5} = 100.0° \qquad [a]_{546}^{22.5} = 115.9° \qquad [a]_{436}^{22.5} = 207.2°$$

Measurements of the rotation of the acid obtained from the resolution are normally carried out in benzene, in which, fortunately, the rotatory power does not vary with concentration, $[a]_D^{20} = 97°$ ($c = 1$ to 10). The following values have been found for rotations in benzene ($c = 10$) at different wavelengths:

$$[a]_D^{22} = 96.8° \qquad [a]_{578}^{22} = 101.1° \qquad [a]_{546}^{22} = 116.12° \qquad [a]_{436}^{22} = 207.15°$$

When using the Horeau method, it is often useful to measure the rotatory dispersion as a means of confirming the chemical purity of the isolated 2-phenylbutanoic acid.
The rotations of 2-phenylbutanoic acid in different solvents are listed in Table 1.

Table 1: Rotatory power in various solvents of optically pure, liquid 2-phenylbutanoic acid ($l = 1$, $[a]_D^{22} = 96.8$).

Solvent	$[a]_D^{22}$ (degrees)
Benzene[a]	96.8
Ethanol[a]	77.4
Chloroform[a]	74.8
Pyridine[a]	112.7
Triethylamine[a]	46.8
1N Sodium hydroxide[a]	9.19

[a] $c = 10$

It should be noted that the rotatory power of 2-phenylbutanoate, as in the case of the sodium or amine salts, is substantially smaller than that of the non-ionized acid.
The other reagent which is fundamental to the method of partial resolution is 2-phenylbutanoic anhydride; this is prepared in the classical manner by heating a mixture of 2-phenylbutanoic acid and acetic anhydride and distilling off the correct amount of acetic acid formed in the dehydration process. The generated anhydride is redistilled; it is colored at this stage, but the color gradually disappears. It has been shown that this color is due to the formation of a small amount of phenyl-

[14] M. Delepine and F. Lareze, Bull. Soc. Chim. France 1955, 104.

[15] K. Petterson, Ark. Kemi 10, 283 (1956).

[16] G. Balavoine and H.B. Kagan, C.R. Acad. Sci., Paris 272, 1511 (1971).

ethyl ketene by the reversible reaction described by Eq. (4) (this small amount of ketene in the freshly distilled anhydride can be detected by infrared spectroscopy[16]).

$$H_5C_6-\underset{\underset{H_5C_2}{|}}{CH}-CO-O-CO-\underset{\underset{C_2H_5}{|}}{CH}-C_6H_5 \rightleftharpoons \underset{\underset{H_5C_2}{/}}{\overset{\overset{H_5C_6}{\diagdown}}{C}}=C=O \;+\; H_5C_6-\underset{\underset{H_5C_2}{|}}{CH}-COOH \tag{4}$$

The anhydride thus obtained by distillation should theoretically consist of a mixture of the *meso* and *threo* diastereoisomers. Examination of the NMR spectrum of a solution of the anhydride in benzene establishes that both of the diastereoisomers are present in essentially equal amounts[17] (see p. 75). Optically active 2-phenylbutanoic acid is perfectly stable in pyridine solution, and its rotation does not vary over a period of several months. The same is not true for the anhydride, however, and the rotation of solutions in pyridine decreases slowly. Moreover, it is impossible to prepare the optically active anhydride by the same procedure as is used for the *racemic* anhydride: the reversible reaction (4) results in racemization. The optically active anhydride can be conveniently prepared by addition of a limited amount of oxalyl chloride to a suspension of the anhydrous sodium salt of optically active 2-phenylbutanoic acid in ether. If the starting material is of sufficient optical purity, the anhydride obtained can be crystallized in the cold from pentane containing a small amount of ether; recrystallization from pure pentane then gives anhydride with $[a]_D^{20}=147°$. Hydrolysis of this anhydride in aqueous dioxane (non-racemizing conditions) yields 2-phenylbutanoic acid with a rotation of 95° and hence an optical purity of

$$\frac{95 \times 100}{97} = 98\%.$$

The maximum rotation of the anhydride should therefore be

$$[a]_D^{20} = \frac{147 \times 97}{95} = 150°.$$

2-Phenylbutanoyl chloride can be prepared under similar conditions, either by treatment of the sodium salt of optically active 2-phenylbutanoic acid with *excess* of oxalyl chloride, or by reaction of the free acid with oxalyl chloride in benzene solution. The acid chloride can be distilled, and the rotation of the optically pure product is $[a]_D^{20} = 105°$ in benzene and $[a]_D^{20} = 100°$ $(l=1)$ in the liquid state.

2-Phenylbutanoic anhydride racemizes in pyridine solution, and the optical activity of a 0.1 molar solution decreases by half in about 20 hr. The acid chloride also racemizes, but at a much greater rate, and a molar solution in pyridine is completely racemized in a few minutes[8].

The various phenomena involved in partial resolution can be illustrated by Eq. (5), in which it can be seen that, in pyridine solution, the *meso* and *threo* anhydrides are in equilibrium due to the formation of an intermediate acylpyridinium carboxylate, although the extent of ion-pair forma-

$$2\;\underset{\underset{Q_l-\overset{\diagdown}{C}\diagdown}{\overset{O}{\parallel}}}{\overset{\overset{O}{\parallel}}{Q_d-C}} \;+\; 2\,N \rightleftharpoons \;\left[\begin{array}{c} Q_l-\overset{O}{\overset{\parallel}{C}}\overset{\oplus}{\underset{N}{}} \\ Q_d-COO^{\ominus} \\ + \\ Q_l-COO^{\ominus} \\ Q_d-\overset{O}{\overset{\parallel}{C}}\overset{\oplus}{\underset{N}{}} \end{array} \right] \rightleftharpoons \; 2\,N \;+\; \begin{array}{c} Q_d-\overset{O}{\overset{\parallel}{C}}\diagdown \\ Q_d-\overset{\diagdown}{C}\diagup \\[4pt] Q_l-\overset{O}{\overset{\parallel}{C}}\diagdown \\ Q_l-\overset{\diagdown}{C}\diagup \end{array} \tag{5}$$

tion is very small. Because the equilibrium is strongly displaced in favor of the anhydrides, the infrared spectrum of the *racemic* anhydride in pyridine solution is similar to that of the anhydride recorded in the absence of pyridine. In the case of the *racemic* acid chloride, however, the infrared spectrum in pyridine solution is completely different from that recorded in the neat liquid. Given that the facile racemization proceeds via formation of such pyridinium ions, it follows that the acid chloride should racemize rapidly and the anhydride much more slowly. This means that the concentration of pyridinium ions in the case of the anhydride is very low, even though it is almost certainly the same pyridinium ions which are the active intermediates in the acylation of alcohols.

One important aspect of the reaction which must be taken into consideration in the use of this method is illustrated by the following data: when one equivalent of 2-phenylbutanoic acid of optical purity 91% ($[a]_D^{20} = 88.1°$ neat, $l = 1$) and one equivalent of the corresponding *racemic* anhydride are dissolved in pyridine, the rotation of the mixture changes in the following manner:

Time [min]	4	10	20	50	60	120	360	6000
Rotation [degrees]	3.744	4.100	4.293	4.308	4.286	4.230	3.800	1.940

These changes can be illustrated graphically as shown in Fig. 2, using two different time scales.

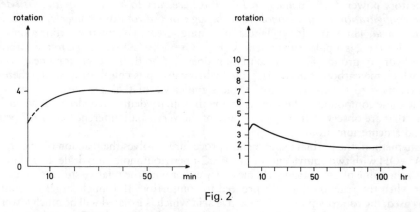

Fig. 2

The increase in the rotation shown in Fig. 2 corresponds to the conversion of part of the *racemic* anhydride into *optically active* anhydride, the molecular rotation of which is higher than that of the acid, according to the equilibrium:

$$Q_d-COOH \quad + \quad Q_d-CO-O-CO-Q_l \quad \rightleftharpoons \quad Q_l-COOH \quad + \quad Q_d-CO-O-CO-Q_d$$

an the phenomenon is accounted for by Eq. (5). Moreover, as this increase in rotation can also be observed in neutral solvents such as benzene, it is reasonable to assume that under these conditions one of the carbonyl groups of the anhydride suffers nucleophilic attack by the carboxylate anion (Eq. (6), even a very small amount of ionization is sufficient to initiate the equilibrium).

$$
\begin{array}{c}
Q_l-\overset{O}{\underset{}{\overset{\|}{C}}}-O-\overset{O}{\underset{}{\overset{\|}{C}}}-Q_d \\
Q_d-\overset{}{\underset{O}{\overset{\|}{C}}}-O^{\ominus}
\end{array}
\quad \rightleftharpoons \quad
\begin{array}{c}
Q_l-\overset{O}{\underset{}{\overset{\|}{C}}}-O^{\ominus} \\
Q_d-\overset{}{\underset{O}{\overset{\|}{C}}}-O-\overset{}{\underset{O}{\overset{\|}{C}}}-Q_d
\end{array}
\qquad (6)
$$

[17] J.P. Vigneron, M. Dhaenens, and A. Horeau, Tetrahedron **29**, 1055 (1973).   [18] H. Falk and K. Schlögl, Monatsh. Chem. **96**, 276 (1965).

This particular phenomenon is of great importance in the Horeau method. In practice, one equivalent of the alcohol under investigation is treated in pyridine solution with two equivalents of 2-phenylbutyric anhydride; after complete esterification of the alcohol there remain one equivalent of acid and one equivalent of anhydride which are in equilibrium as shown by Eq. (6). If the acid which is formed is isolated by extraction with base, but without prior hydrolysis of the excess[a] anhydride, then the optical yield which is obtained will be an *underestimate*. The anhydride, in which some of the optical activity of the acid has been incorporated, is not in fact destroyed under the reaction conditions used and remains in the organic phase. In Ref. [18], the optical purity found for (–)-menthol is 23% instead of 40%.

Examination of a plot such as that shown in Fig. 2 shows, on the other hand, that, after a certain time, it becomes a straight line, the slope of which is characteristic of the amount of optically active anhydride (for a solution in pyridine at a given temperature). This particular aspect has been employed in a variation of the method which involves following of the rotatory power of the mixture of the alcohol and the *racemic* anhydride in pyridine for a sufficiently long time.

1.7.   Significance of the Optical Yield

The value of the optical yield is a very important figure when it is used in conjunction with the observed rotatory power. *If this value is < 15% it is necessary to be very careful when deducing the absolute configuration of an alcohol from the sign of the rotatory power of the isolated 2-phenylbutanoic acid.* This is true for cyclanols containing several asymmetric carbon atoms and for alcohols in which there is a polar substituent $(C_6H_5, -C=C-, -CO-R, etc.)$ *a* to the carbon atom carrying the hydroxy group. The same situation does not hold, however, for linear secondary alcohols in which the carbon atom bearing the hydroxy group is chiral, or in which there are no polar substituents *a* to the hydroxy group; the significance of the very small optical yields is maintained in these compounds. The same is true with primary deuterated alcohols, where the low optical yields that are observed are a consequence of the very small difference in "size" between a hydrogen and a deuterium atom.

In the Horeau method, the normal experimental procedure involves the reaction of one equivalent of alcohol A*–OH with two equivalents of *racemic* 2-phenylbutanoic anhydride. It is of interest to examine how the value of the optical yield may vary either with the relative stoichiometry of these reactants or when the reaction does not proceed to completion. If a much larger amount of the anhydride is used, the rotatory power of the active acid which is isolated will be much lower due to dilution by the acid produced during hydrolysis of the excess anhydride. The *optical yield,* on the other hand, calculated as described previously, will be larger. As can be seen from Scheme 1, the speed v_2 with which B reacts with A* depends both on the rate constant k, which is characteristic for the reaction, and on the concentration of A°. Since a racemate is involved, the initial concentrations of A*, and of A° are identical; if A* is consumed more rapidly than A°, then the concentration of A*, and hence the ratio of concentrations C_{A^*}/C_{A°, will also decrease more rapidly. The ratio of the rates of the reactions will also decrease more rapidly in turn, as these are directly derived from the concentrations. When the amount of A is very large with respect to B, however, this effect can be neglected. The optical yield would also be expected to increase when the ratio N/n increases. From the data listed in Table 2, however, it can be seen that only a small effect is observed. Reaction of equal amounts of the alcohol A*–OH with the *threo* anhydride [n = N, as in (3a)], on the other hand, might be expected to result in the formation of an acid of zero rotation. Indeed, even in the case of a highly stereoselective reaction, rapid disappearance of the anhydride *l,l* must inevitably be followed by a slower disappearance of the anhydride *d,d*, and the overall effect should be manifested in the formation of equal amounts of dextro- and laevo-rotatory acids. In practice, however, the optical yield of a pyridine solution of menthol (0.2 mol) and of 2-phenylbu-

---

[a] A phrase was unfortunately omitted in the first publications in the series, p. 511, line 8: "after several hours, the reaction mixture is hydrolyzed by the addition of a little water, and poured into a separatory funnel containing benzene…" (this necessary additional phrase is mentioned in subsequent papers).

tanoic acid (0.2 mol) is still considerable (see Table 2b). Further diminution of the anhydride/alcohol ratio results in only a small variation in the optical yield (Table 2c). These results can be

Table 2: Reaction of d,l-2-phenylbutanoic anhydride with $(-)$-menthol in pyridine

Time	Optical yield calculated from the rotatory power of the isolated acid	Optical yield calculated from the GLC areas	Esterification Yield [%]	Number of molecules of $(-)$-menthol[a]
a) Anhydride/menthol ratio 2:1				
15 min	53.7	53.7	22	11
2 hr	47.9	49	71	35.5
20 hr	38.6	47	100	50
b) Anhydride/menthol ratio 1:1				
15 min	53.7	53.5	25.5	25.5
1 hr	48.5	48.2	49	49
3 hr	43.2	44	69	69
20 hr	38.5	42	90.5	90.5
c) Anhydride/menthol ratio 1:2				
21 hr	35.7	40	93	93

[a] menthol molecules which have effectively reacted with 100 molecules of anhydride

satisfactorily explained by assuming that the 2-phenylbutanoic anhydride exists uniquely in the meso form, Q_d-CO-O-CO-Q_l. Obviously, under these conditions, and irrespective of how far the reaction has proceeded, the two antipodal constituents are always present in equal amounts while, on the other hand, the optical yield is independent of the relative proportions of anhydride and alcohol [see Eqs. (3a) and (3b) p. 56]. This cannot, however, completely explained with the effect because, as was mentioned earlier, the anhydride which is prepared by normal procedures contains equal amounts of the *meso* and *threo* forms[17]. Moreover, the ions Q_d-COO$^\ominus$, Q_l-COO$^\ominus$, Q_d-CO-$\overset{\oplus}{N}C_5H_5$ and Q_l-CO-$\overset{\oplus}{N}C_5H_5$ are present in pyridine solution, and, as can be seen from the equilibria of Eq. (7) [which is derived from Eq. (5)] the anionic species Q_d-COO$^\ominus$ can be transformed into the cationic species Q-CO-$\overset{\oplus}{N}C_5H_5$. The results described previously can then be understood in terms of these equilibria, given that the acylpyridinium intermediate functions as the

$$Q_d\text{-}C\overset{O}{\underset{O^\ominus}{\big\|}} \ + \ Q_l\text{-}C\overset{O}{\underset{\overset{\oplus}{N=}}{\big\|}} \ \rightleftarrows \ \overset{Q_d\text{-}C\overset{O}{\diagdown_O}}{\underset{Q_l\text{-}C\diagup_O}{}} \ \rightleftarrows \ Q_d\text{-}C\overset{O}{\underset{\overset{\oplus}{N=}}{\big\|}} \ + \ Q_l\text{-}C\overset{O}{\underset{O^\ominus}{\big\|}} \tag{7}$$

acylating agent. Consequently, it is fortunately possible to compare the optical yields for various alcohols, even if the reactions do not go to completion or if the alcohol/anhydride ratios are not always the same.

Table 3: Optical yield determined by GLC as a function of the number of molecules N of $(-)$-menthol which have effectively reacted in presence of 100 molecules of d,l-anhydride in pyridine.

N	11	25	35	49	50	69	90.5	93
Optical yield [%]	53.7	53.5	49	48.2	47	44	42	40

It can be seen from the data in Table 2 that when the reaction time is short, the same value for the optical yield is obtained from the two different types of measurement, i.e. from the rotatory power of the isolated acid, and from the GLC estimation of the relative amounts of diastereoisomeric esters formed. The variation between the two methods, which increases with reaction time, is the result of racemization and becomes more and more important. The most interesting figures listed in Table 2, however, are those shown in the last column, namely the relative numbers of molecules of (–)-menthol which have effectively esterified during the reaction. These data for N have been arranged in increasing order in Table 3, from which it can be seen that there is a corresponding regular decrease in the values of the optical yields (although the absolute difference between the extreme values is relatively small).

The value of the optical yield is a suitable indication of the "size" of the groups R and R' in an alcohol R–CHOH–R' (except in instances where one of these groups is aromatic; such compounds constitute a special case, and will be discussed on p. 66). Thus, for secondary alcohols of the general type H_3C–CHOH–R the optical yields are:

R=CH_2–CH_3, 8.5%; R=$CH(CH_3)_2$, 42%; and R=$C(CH_3)_3$, 49%.

These data clearly illustrate how the optical yield increases as the steric environment of the methyl group changes with respect to the ethyl, isopropyl and t-butyl groups[8].

When R is a linear alkyl substituent, a slight increase in optical yield is to be expected as the number of carbon atoms in the chain increases; starting from R=C_2H_5, where the yield is 8.5%, the value tends toward a limit of 16% for R=C_9H_{19}. Consequently, if the value measured for a given alcohol within this series, e.g. H_3C–CHOH–C_5H_{11}, is significantly lower than the above figures, it follows that the material cannot be optically pure, and its approximate optical purity can be calculated. This approach has been used frequently, and in certain cases has furnished approximate values for the optical purities of alcohols. In cases where there is a similar arrangement of substituents with respect to the secondary hydroxy groups in two different molecules, it is predictable that the optical yields for the two molecules will be in the same region, as for example in 3β-hydroxy-17a-(1-hydroxyethyl)-17β-methyl-18-nor-5a-androst-13-ene(4) and 3-hydroxy-2,2-dimethylbutane (5), where the observed optical yields are 60 and 49%, respectively[3, 8]. Similarly, resolution of *all-trans* C/D ring-fused 17β-hydroxy steroids with 2-phenylbutanoic acid proceeds with optical yields in the range of 40–45%; the same is true for the tricyclic alcohol 6. If the optical yield found for the latter compound is considerably smaller than 40–45%, then it follows that the material is either of low optical purity or that the structure has been incorrectly assigned. There are many examples of the application of such arguments.

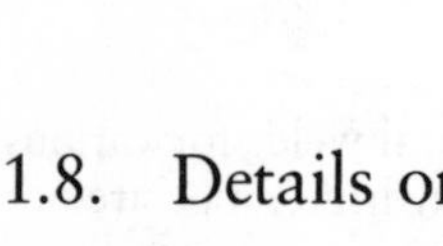

4 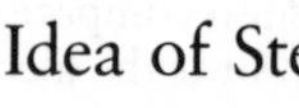   5 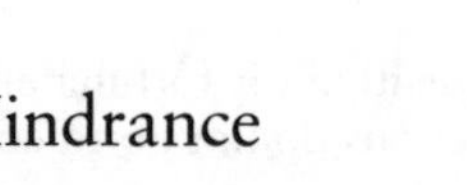   6   7

1.8.   Details on the Idea of Steric Hindrance

As a result of detailed investigations with alcohols of known configurations, the following order as regards the steric hindrance of various groups, classified as L and M (see p. 54), has been found:

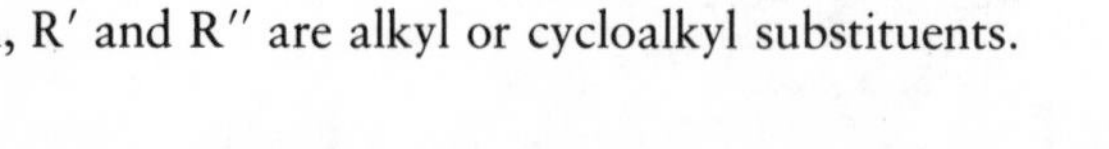

where R, R' and R" are alkyl or cycloalkyl substituents.

Nevertheless, it is valid to investigate whether, in certain cases, the extent of substitution at the two carbon atoms adjacent to the carbon carrying the secondary hydroxy group affords sufficient information on the steric situation at the chiral center. Consider the chiral cyclopentanol A*:

A'   A*   A°

There is no overall change in the steric situation when the orientation of the hydroxy group is changed, A' and A* are identical and A° is the antipode. Consider now the closely related cyclopentanols B and C:

B   C   D

When the orientation of the hydroxy group in B is reversed, the *epimeric* alcohol C is obtained. It is clear that, as in the preceding example, the steric situations in B and C are identical with respect to the carbon atoms adjacent to the chiral center. Consequently, partial resolution of two such *epimeric* alcohols would be expected to result in the formation of 2-phenylbutanoic acid of the same sign. This general situation should exist for all cases of complex molecules where the overall steric hindrance, which can influence the rate of esterification of a secondary alcohol, has the same origin for each of the epimers. In other cases, however, where the steric effect of an a-substituent is not very great, the observed resolution can be derived from steric effects in other parts of the molecule. Thus, in a cycloalkanol of the general type D, the steric effect of the R' group can be significantly greater than that of the R group[5].

1.8.1. Steric Hindrance in the case of Long-Distance Effects

One notable example of this effect is found with (+)-epiisoborneol (9), resolution of which with *racemic* 2-phenylbutanoic anhydride results in the predominant formation of dextrorotatory acid

8   9

(optical yield 5%), which has the same sign as the acid obtained on resolution of the epimeric *endo* alcohol, (−)-epiborneol (8) (optical yield 35%). From an examination of molecular models, it can be seen that this apparent anomaly is due to the additional steric effect of the C-9 methyl group in 9.

A particularly clear-cut example of this phenomenon is found in the 11-hydroxy steroids 10 and 11, where also both of the *epimeric* alcohols are preferentially esterified by one enantiomer of 2-phenylbutyric acid[19]. The optical yields for 10 and 11 are +28 and +65%, respectively, showing that in both cases a strong left hindrance (Fig. 1). Examination of Dreiding models shows clearly that in 10 the steric hindrance can be accounted for in terms of the a-substituents (the C-9−C-10 and C-10−C-1 bonds). In the epimer 11, on the other hand, the substituent which is antiparallel to the hydroxy group has little steric effect; steric hindrance in the esterification is provided by the C-18 methyl group which is 1,3-*diaxial* with respect to the hydroxy group.

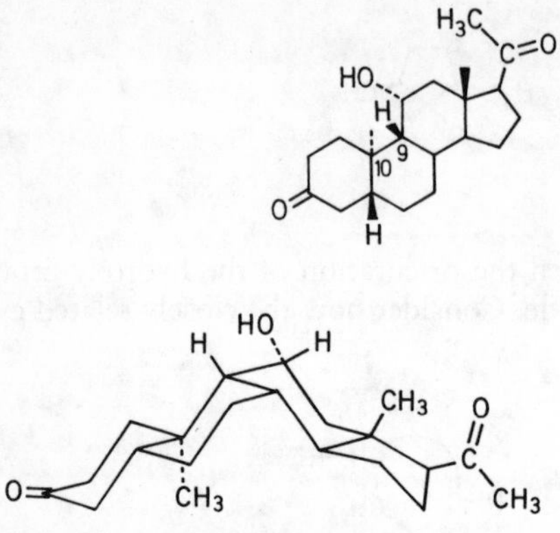

10 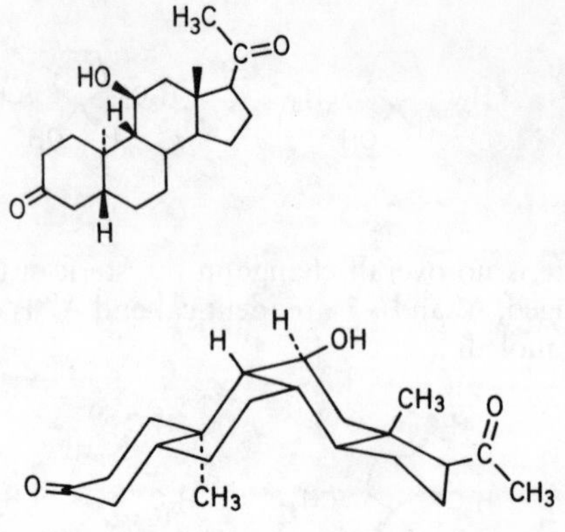   11

In the case of a complex chiral molecule where the secondary group is flanked by two methylene groups, conclusions may only be drawn if the optical yield is significant (> 15%) and if examination of three dimensional models reveals the nature of the steric hindrance.

Derivatives of 3-hydroxy steroids have been studied in detail[20], and it is remarkable that, depending on the nature of the substitution at the remote C-17 position, the resolution can be either positive or negative, varying in the range −3.1 to +1.8%. The method described in the present chapter, however, cannot be applied to this particular case.

1.8.2. Steric Hindrance in "Benzylic" Alcohols

As previously, the concept of "size", or steric hindrance, often accounts perfectly adequately for observed results. It is sometimes necessary, however, to consider more complex effects such as the "polarity" of substituents. In the subsequent discussion dealing with the comparison of priorities which result from experimental observations, the conventional terms "large" (L) and "medium" (M) are used.

A striking illustration of the apparent concept of steric size is provided by linear alkylphenylcarbinols 12, resolution of which with 2-phenylbutanoic anhydride proceeds such that the phenyl group always appears to be the "largest", while the optical yield varies very little with the nature of R, even through R = CH_3, *t*-butyl or triphenylmethyl[8]. In the case of R = triphenylmethyl, the greater "volume" of this group relative to a phenyl group should lead to a decrease in the difference between the "sizes" of the two groups, and to a reduction in the value of the optical yield. Because of their "polarity", aromatic groups cannot be classified solely on the basis of the concept of "steric hindrance".

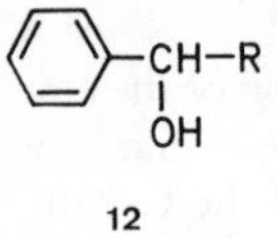

12   13

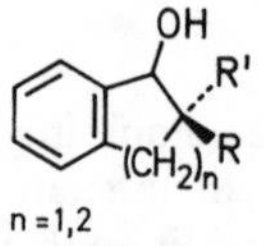

The situation can, however, be different with benzocyclanols of type 13, where the R group is now a substituent in a carbocyclic system which is fused to the aromatic ring, as in 2-substituted

[19] G. Saucy, H. Els, F. Miksch, and A. Fürst, Helv. Chim. Acta 49, 1529 (1966).

[20] G. Balavoine, A. Horeau, J.P. Jacquet, and H.B. Kagan, Bull. Soc. Chim. France 1970, 1910.

indanols and tetralols. As a result of the investigations of such compounds during which it was necessary to establish the absolute configurations of the alcohols employed in an independent and unambiguous manner, it has been shown that

when n = 1 or n = 2, R = R′ = H, the phenyl group is "larger"[21]
when n = 1 or n = 2, R = R′ = CH$_3$, the phenyl group is "medium"[21]
when n = 2, R = H, R′ = CH$_3$ (cis or trans), the phenyl group is also "medium"[22]

and these results can be understood by examination of molecular models.
It is also of interest to consider a further structural modification of 1-hydroxytetralins, namely 15. In contrast to the situation with 1-hydroxytetralin (14) where the aryl substituent is the "large"

group, introduction of two methyl substituents in the 5- and 8-position to give 15 changes the aryl substituent to a "medium" group. This result follows indisputably from the fact that the acetates of the alcohols derived from 14 and 15 by partial resolution with enantiomeric 2-phenylbutanoic acids have the same absolute configuration. Moreover, oxidation of these two acetates with ruthenium(IV) oxide gives 2-acetoxyadipic acid, the sign of which is the same in each case[23]. This apparent anomaly can be explained in terms of the steric constraints imposed on the fused cyclohexane ring by the methyl substituents on the aromatic ring[24]. This same explanation cannot, however, be applied to the alcohols 16 and 17. The absolute configurations of 16 and 17 have been determined[25] by the partial resolution method, and the R and S configurations assigned to the

carbon atoms carrying the hydroxy groups in the exo and endo isomers, respectively. The absolute configuration of [2,2]paracyclophane-4-carboxylic acid (18), the precursor of the alcohols 16 and 17, has been determined by X-ray analysis[25, 26]. Thus, in the case of the alcohols 16 and 17 it seems that the paracyclophane substituent is the large group.

[21] P. Briaucourt, J.P. Guetté, and A. Horeau, C.R. Acad. Sci., Paris 274, 1203 (1972).

[22] A. Schoofs, J.P. Guetté, and A. Horeau, C.R. Acad. Sci., Paris 274, 1527 (1972).

[23] R. Weidmann and J.P. Guetté, C.R. Acad. Sci., Paris 268, 2225 (1969); R. Weidmann, M. Perlat, and J.P. Guetté (unpubl. results).

[24] P. Briaucourt, Thèse d'Université Paris, June, 1972; J.P. Guetté, P. Briaucourt, and A. Horeau (unpubl. results).

[25] H. Falk, P. Reich-Rohrwig, and K. Schlögl, Tetrahedron 26, 511 (1970).

[26] J. Tribout, R.H. Martin, M. Doyle, and H. Wynberg, Tetrahedron Lett. 28, 2839 (1972), and references quoted.

[27] J.F. King and S.K. Sim, J. Amer. Chem. Soc. 95, 4448 (1973).

2.　Scope of the Reaction

2.1.　Determination of the Absolute Configurations of the Enantiomers of a *racemic* Alcohol

Consider the *racemic* alcohol A_d–OH + A_l–OH: treatment of this racemate with less than the stoichiometric amount of optically active 2-phenylbutanoic anhydride (for example the dextrorotatory isomer) under the same conditions as described previously (see p.55) will result in resolution of the alcohol according to the following general scheme:

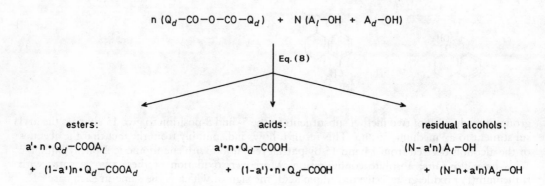

$$n\,(Q_d{-}CO{-}O{-}CO{-}Q_d) \quad + \quad N\,(A_l{-}OH \ + \ A_d{-}OH)$$

Eq. (8)

esters:

$a' \cdot n \cdot Q_d{-}COOA_l$

$+\ (1{-}a')n \cdot Q_d{-}COOA_d$

acids:

$a' \cdot n \cdot Q_d{-}COOH$

$+\ (1{-}a') \cdot n \cdot Q_d{-}COOH$

residual alcohols:

$(N{-}\,a'n)\,A_l{-}OH$

$+\ (N{-}n{+}a'n)\,A_d{-}OH$

It can readily be shown that a′ [Eq. (8)] is equal to a [Eqs. (3a) and (3b), p. 56][7]. Indeed, the characteristic rate constant for the reaction of the dextrorotatory pyridinium ion $Q_d{-}CO{-}\overset{\oplus}{N}C_5H_5$ with the A_d-OH antipode of the alcohol in a given medium at a given temperature is identical to the characteristic rate constant for reaction of the laevorotatory ion $Q_l{-}CO{-}\overset{\oplus}{N}C_5H_5$ with the alcohol A_l-OH, which has been verified experimentally[8, 10]. Consequently, these reactions do not involve "non-reciprocal kinetic resolution"[27]. Moreover, the residual alcohol which is isolated after the reactions shown in Eq. (8) will be optically active, as A_d-OH will be present in excess over A_l-OH. From a practical point of view, the work up procedure is somewhat more difficult than that involved in the general method previously described, as it necessitates separation of the residual alcohol from the corresponding diastereoisomeric esters. The separation, however, need not necessarily be quantitative; only a certain amount of the alcohol, uncontaminated with esters, has to be isolated (without any change in optical composition) and its rotatory power to be measured. Three practical procedures have been used for this separation[8]:

(1) Separation by distillation. This method has been employed in many cases, and the chemical purity of the isolated alcohols has been confirmed by GLC.
(2) Separation by column chromatography (e.g. on alumina).
(3) Reaction of the alcohol with phthalic anhydride to form the semi-ester of phthalic acid and subsequent separation of this intermediate from other esters by extraction with base.

The following empirical rule applies to such resolution:
When dextrorotatory 2-phenylbutanoic anhydride is used, the alcohol, which is defined by the sign ascertained after separation, has the configuration shown in **19**.

19

This assignment follows immediately from the considerations outlined above, since the dextrorotatory acid reacts faster with the A*–OH alcohol and hence the reaction afford an excess of the A°–OH alcohol. Development of this method requires preparation of the optically active 2-phenylbutanoic anhydrides (for details see experimental section, p. 76). It is not, however, necessary to employ the optically pure anhydride. The optical purity of the anhydride need only be sufficient for practical resolution; in the calculation of the optical yield a correction can be made based on the rotatory power of the residual 2-phenylbutanoic acid which results from the esterification. This acid can be isolated by extraction with a base and its rotatory power compared with the known maximum value of 96.8° for the optically pure acid under defined conditions.

2.2.   Primary Deuterated Alcohols

Primary deuterated alcohols of the type R–CHD–OH are chiral compounds; they can therefore exist in two enantiomeric forms, and it is of interest to know the absolute configurations of these enantiomers. However, the question arises whether the partial resolution method using an optically active primary deuterated alcohol R–CDH–OH will afford an acid with a measurable optical activity. This does not, at first sight, appear to be a very promising possibility. Thus, it has been shown, that partial asymmetric reduction of a *racemic* biphenylyl ketone by optically pure H_3C–CHOH–CD_3 under Meerwein-Ponndorf-Verley conditions does not result in any detectable asymmetric induction, even though the procedure used was very precise[28]. Nevertheless, the partial resolution method can be applied to alcohols of the type R–CDH–OH as a result of the following considerations. 2-Phenylbutanoic acid has a rotatory power of $\sim 100°$ while a rotation of 0.005° can be readily measured. A simple calculation shows that if k_1 is the rate constant for the esterification reaction of a primary deuterated alcohol with the dextrorotatory acid and k_2 the rate constant for the same reaction with laevorotatory acid, it is possible to detect an "optical yield" of 0.015%, which corresponds to a ratio of $k_1/k_2 = 1.003$.

$$R-\underset{\underset{D}{|}}{C}H-OH \ + \ HOOC-Q_d \ \xrightarrow{k_1} \ R-\underset{\underset{D}{|}}{C}H-O-CO-Q_d$$

$$R-\underset{\underset{D}{|}}{C}H-OH \ + \ HOOC-Q_l \ \xrightarrow{k_2} \ R-\underset{\underset{D}{|}}{C}H-O-CO-Q_l$$

Consequently, the partial resolution method is a highly sensitive procedure.

It has been confirmed experimentally that a *measurable* resolution can be obtained by reaction of an optically active primary deuterated alcohol with an excess of *racemic* 2-phenylbutanoic anhydride[13]. In one such investigation the optical yield, has been found as 0.5%, which corresponds to a rate ratio of 1.01. On a 0.002 molar scale, the rotation of the acid isolated is $[a]_D^{20} = \pm 0.080°$ ($l = 1$) showing that the rotation can be observed with a reasonable degree of accuracy. Similar investigation of the secondary alcohol (+)-S-2-propanol-1-d_3, the chirality of which is derived from the presence of the deuterium atoms a to the hydroxy function, however also results in resolution and gives an optical yield in the region 0.4 to 0.5%. The absolute configuration of this alcohol is known, as it has been prepared from (+)-lactic acid. Consequently, it must be concluded that *deuterium is small* compared to hydrogen; this conclusion is in agreement with other experimental results.

With respect to the scope of the empirical rule established earlier, it can be stated that in the case of a primary deuterated alcohol, the deuterium atom must be considered as the small, "S", group and the hydrogen atom as the medium "M", group, as shown in 20. The new empirical rule covering such compounds is then: "*When esterification of an optically active primary deuterated alcohol by*

---

[28] K. Mislow, R.E. O'Brien, and H. Schäffer, J. Amer. Chem. Soc. **82**, 5512 (1960); **84**, 1940 (1962).   [29] R.H. Mazur, J. Org. Chem. 35, 2050 (1970).

means of an excess of racemic 2-phenylbutanoic anhydride in anhydrous pyridine solution results in the formation of laevorotatory 2-phenylbutanoic acid, the alcohol has the configuration R^a.

a This is an exceptional general case where the designation R or S can be related to the sign of the isolated acid as the order of priority is always OH > carbon substituent > D > H

2.3.   Amines

The reactions of primary amines with anhydrides are analogous to those of alcohols. It has therefore been investigated whether the partial resolution method developed for alcohols can be extended to amines and whether an empirical rule can thus be formulated for these substrates. Initial investigations in a number of favorable cases have indicated that such an extension may be possible[8], but it subsequently became rapidly apparent that there would be numerous exceptions to any general method; therefore, *the partial resolution method does not apply to primary amines*. It is, however, quite predictable that, with respect to a homologous series of amines, the 2-phenylbutanoic acid produced as a result of the amide forming reaction will have the same sign when amines of the same absolute configuration are employed. This approach has been utilized for the determination of the absolute configuration of several 1-methylalkylamines[29]. Experimentally, the procedure involves resolution of 2-phenylbutanoic acid by treatment with chiral amines in dichloromethane in the presence of dicyclohexylcarbodiimide. Both primary and secondary amines have been resolved by the use of S(+)-2-phenylpropanoic acid[30]. The configuration of the amine which did not react with the acid was found to be **21**, and the relative size of groups was found to be benzyl > phenyl, 2-tolyl > phenyl, and naphthyl > benzyl > methyl. 1-Phenylethylamine, unfortunately

$$
\begin{array}{c}
\text{M} \\
| \\
\text{H}\!-\!\!-\!\!-\!\!-\!\!-\!\!\text{NH}\!-\!\text{R} \\
| \\
\text{L} \\
\textbf{21}
\end{array}
$$

proved to be an exception to this general order; this result emphasises that great care must be taken in the interpretation of the absolute configurations of chiral amines when these are determined by partial resolution.

However, satisfactory results are obtained with amines when an acylating agent prepared from 2-phenylbutanoic acid and imidazole is used[31].

3.   Variation in the Conditions of Esterification Leading to Kinetic Resolution

A number of interesting results have been obtained from studies in which a secondary, enantiomerically pure alcohol has been employed as a standard and in which either the esterifying anhydride or the reaction medium has been varied. The secondary alcohol selected by Horeau for

[30] O. Cervinka, V. Dudek, Collect. Czech. Chem. Commun. **38**, 1159 (1973).

[31] H. Brockmann and N. Risch, Angew. Chem. **13**, 664 (1974).

these investigations was natural (−)-menthol and the choice was based on two major grounds. Firstly, adequate amounts of very pure products can readily be obtained, and secondly, the optical yield under normal operating conditions (2-phenylbutanoic anhydride in pyridine) is of the order of 50%.

3.1. Replacement of 2-Phenylbutanoic Acid by Other Acids

Reactions of (−)-menthol with various other acids (as the corresponding anhydrides) are carried out in anhydrous pyridine under the usual conditions of stoichiometry.

In view of the excellent results obtained with 2-phenylbutanoic acid, the potential utility of other 2-phenylalkanecarboxylic acids, and in particular of 2-phenylpropanoic acid (hydratropic acid) has been investigated. This compound was especially interesting to compare with 2-phenylbutanoic acid, as the difference in "size" between a methyl and a phenyl group is greater than that between an ethyl and a phenyl group. In practice, however, this simple argument does not hold, and the optical yields with hydratropic acid are not as good as those with 2-phenylbutanoic acid. The results obtained for

$$H_5C_6-\underset{\underset{R}{|}}{CH}-COOH$$

where $R = CH_3$, C_2H_5, C_3H_7, and $CH(CH_3)_2$ are listed in Table 4[32].

One interesting feature of the results obtained in this study is that when R is isopropyl, the corresponding optically active anhydride undergoes racemization about ten times more slowly than 2-phenylbutanoic anhydride. This phenomenon consequently raised the interesting possibility that completion of the esterification process could be effected with the former anhydride simply by allowing the reaction to proceed longer and that would then not be necessary to make the usual correction to account for the extent of esterification. Unfortunately, the rate of esterification of (−)-menthol with 3-methyl-2-phenylbutanoic anhydride

$$\left(H_5C_6-\underset{\underset{CH(CH_3)_2}{|}}{CH}-CO-\right)_2 O$$

was also found to be about ten times slower than the rate of esterification with 2-phenylbutanoic anhydride, and thus there is no overall advantage in using the isopropyl compound. It appears to be general within this series of compounds that the rates of esterification and of racemization are of the same order.

Comparison of the optical yields obtained from the reactions of (−)-menthol with various 2-phenylalkanecarboxylic anhydrides is carried out by determination of the peak areas of the two diastereoisomeric esters of (−)-menthol by GLC.

Table 4:

$$\left(H_5C_6-\underset{\underset{R}{|}}{CH}-CO\right)_2 O + (-)\text{-Menthol} \longrightarrow \text{Menthyl esters}$$

2 equiv.   1 equiv.

R	Time of esterification [hr]	Optical Yield [%][a]
CH_3	0.5	43
CH_3	3	39
CH_3	20	34.5
C_2H_5	6	50.8
C_2H_5	16	49
C_3H_7	16	38.5
$CH(CH_3)_2$	16	43

[a] measured by GLC analysis of the esters

From the data listed in Table 4 for the various anhydrides, it can be seen that, provided a sufficient number of examples is studied, this procedure can be used as a method for the determination of the absolute configuration of various acids of the general type R–CHR′–COOH. This has in fact been verified experimentally for derivatives of ferrocene[33, 34] cymantrene[35] and benchrotrene[36] using either (–)-menthol or (–)-1-phenylethylamine as chiral reagent.

3.2.   Influence of the Co-solvent

Esterification of (–)-menthol by *racemic* 2-phenylbutanoic anhydride has been studied in various reaction media. In all of the media studied, reaction has been found to be very slow and the optical yield low in the absence of pyridine or a tertiary base. Consequently, it appears that high optical yields are realized only when ammonium ion formation is possible.

In practice, therefore, reaction is best carried out by addition of a small but adequate amount of a tertiary amine (for example two equivalents per equivalent of anhydride) to a solution of the reactants. It is obviously experimentally advantageous to use as reaction medium a solvent such as dioxane or dimethylformamide, which are miscible with water, as the excess anhydride can then be readily hydrolyzed under homogeneous conditions. Hydrolysis of excess anhydride is, for example, very difficult in benzene solution and requires in this case prolonged stirring with excess water or base. Use of benzene as solvent does afford, however, a method whereby the amount of acid present can be determined even in the presence of the anhydride, and hence the exact extent of esterification can be calculated. Thus, direct and accurate determination of the amount of esterified (–)-menthol can be carried out by addition of a base and phenolphthalein to a benzene solution originally prepared from one equiv. of (–)-menthol, two equiv. of anhydride and four equiv. of pyridine. The optical acitivity of the 2-phenylbutanoic acid produced as a result of esterification can be measured after its isolation in the usual manner.

It is unfortunately impossible to obtain a direct estimate of the optical yield when partial resolution is carried out in benzene as solvent. As pointed out earlier, because of the equilibria which result in exchange (see p. 61), a large part of the optical activity is transferred to the anhydride which, of course, remains in benzene. Addition of methanol (2–4 equiv.) to the benzene solution results in total esterification of the residual anhydride to give equal amounts of the methyl ester and the free acid; the latter compound can then be isolated and its optical acitivity measured. This procedure, which is more complicated than that involved in the classical method, gives similar results for optical yields.

3.3.   Replacement of Pyridine by Other Tertiary Amines

The influence of various tertiary bases on the value of resolution has been studied. Preliminary investigations have been performed with 3β-hydroxy-17-oxoandrostane when pyridine (optical yield 45%) is replaced by a-, β- and γ-picoline; the optical yields are 39, 41 and 44%, respectively. Triethylamine has also been used as a base and the rotation of the acid isolated at the end of the reaction has been found to be zero. In the related case of the diastereoisomeric (–)-menthyl esters, however, the gas chromatograms show that significantly different amounts of diastereoisomers are formed being equivalent to an optical yield of 45%. The only possible explanation for this surprising result with triethylamine is that the acylammonium salt

$$H_5C_6-\underset{\underset{C_2H_5}{|}}{CH}-CO\overset{\oplus}{\underset{\underset{C_2H_5}{|}}{N}}\overset{\overset{C_2H_5}{|}}{{-}}N{-}C_2H_5$$

racemises very rapidly.

---

[32] A. Schoofs and A. Horeau, in preparation.

[33] H. Falk, K. Schlögl, and W. Steyrer, Monatsh. Chem. **97**, 1029 (1966).

[34] H. Falk, O. Hofer, and K. Schlögl, Monatsh. Chem. **100**, 624 (1969).

This has been verified experimentally by observation of the racemization of optically active 2-phenylbutanoic anhydride dissolved in triethylamine. The rate of racemization of 2-phenylbutanoic anhydride by tertiary amines thus depends on the nature of the amine, i.e. on its basicity or nucleophilicity.

In Table 5 are listed the results of a number of experiments carried out with various tertiary amines (chiral and achiral, optically active and optically inactive) both in the presence and absence of pyridine

Table 5: Esterification of (−)-menthol by *racemic* 2-phenylbutanoic anhydride with the aid of various tertiary amines in the presence or absence of pyridine.

	Pyridine	Tertiary amine	Optical yield [%] calculated by: $[a]°$	GLC
	Py	—	45	50
1	—	$N(C_2H_5)_3$	—	19
2	Py	$H_5C_6-N(C_2H_5)_2$	—	42
3	Py	$(+)-H_5C_6-CH-N(CH_3)_2$ CH_3	16,5	50
4	Py	$(-)-H_5C_6-CH-N(CH_3)_2$ CH_3	23	50
5	—	$(-)-H_5C_6-CH-N(CH_3)_2$ CH_3	ε	(∗) 15
6	—	$(\pm)-H_5C_6-CH-N(CH_3)_2$ CH_3	ε	(∗) 16
7	Py	$(\pm)-H_5C_6-CH-N(CH_3)_2$ CH_3	4,2	47
8	—	$H_5C_6-CH_2-N(CH_3)_2$	ε	(∗) 35
9	Py	$(+)-H_5C_6-CH_2-CH-N(CH_3)_2$ CH_3	ε	42

From the data in Table 5[11] it can be seen that in the absence of pyridine, the acid which is isolated has either a low or zero rotation (entries 1, 5, 6, 8), although examination of the esters which are produced gives variable results: in three of the cases, in which the numerical value is preceded by a (∗) sign, more (−)-menthyl (+)-2-phenylbutanoate is formed than (−)-menthyl (−)-2-phenyl-butanoate. Consequently, whenever the amine constituent is changed in the Horeau method, it becomes necessary to devise a new empirical rule for each change, and each new rule should be based on a statistically significant number of examples. It should be noted that, with respect to entries 5 and 6, the same overall result is obtained with either the laevorotatory or the racemic amine, and that the chirality of the amine is not therefore involved in these reactions. The results obtained with the achiral amine dimethylbenzylamine (entry 8) are especially significant.

In all the cases where pyridine is present, however, (entries 2, 3, 4, 7, 9) GLC analysis of the esters reveals that (−)-menthyl (−)-2-phenylbutanoate is formed in the usual excess with respect to its

[35] H. Falk and K. Schlögl, Monatsh. Chem. 99, 578 (1968).   [36] J. Besançon and J. Tirouflet, Bull. Soc. Chim. France 1969, 861.

diastereoisomer. This is very fortunate, as many of the determinations of configurations of carbon atoms in secondary alcohols have been carried out on substrates such as alkaloids (Table 17) which also bear tertiary amino groups. Consequently, inversion of the sign of the isolated acid due to the presence of pyridine does not appear to be a real possibility, although under these conditions the optical yield may well be underestimated. Partial resolution of the steroidal amino-alcohol **22** for example, gives an abnormally low optical yield of 0.5%.

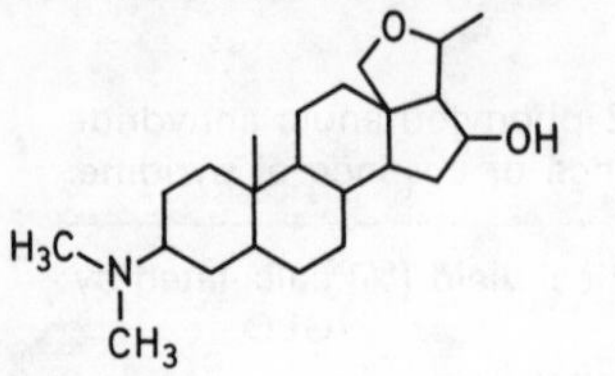

| **22** | **23** |

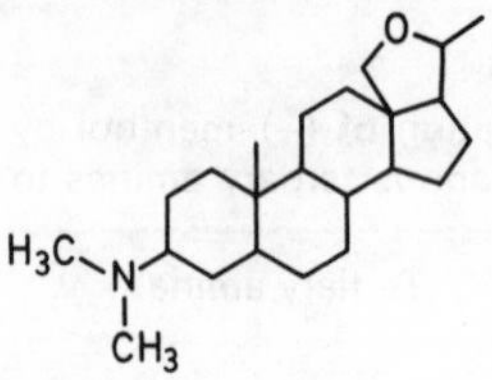

Partial resolution of 17-hydroxy-3-oxoandrostane under the standard conditions has been effected many times; it proceeds with an optical yield of 45%. If this resolution is then carried out in the presence of the amino steroid **23**, the deoxy derivative of **22**, the optical yield falls to 18%, thus demonstrating the intermolecular effect of the dimethylamino group.
The alcohol

$$H_5C_6-\underset{\underset{OH}{|}}{CH}-CH_2-CH_2-N(CH_3)_2$$

has been prepared by asymmetric synthesis and obtained in an optically pure state by resolution[37]. Application of the Horeau method to various samples of this compound lead to an optical yield in the range 10–17%. This value is very low as compared with those obtained for the related alcohols

$$H_5C_6-\underset{\underset{OH}{|}}{CH}-C_2H_5 \ (58.5\%) \quad \text{and} \quad H_5C_6-\underset{\underset{OH}{|}}{CH}-(CH_2)_3-CH_3 \ (52\%)[8]$$

The decrease in the optical yield is again unambiguously due to the presence of the tertiary amino group.
A modification of the partial resolution method[31] uses in place of 2-phenylbutanoic anhydride, the derivative

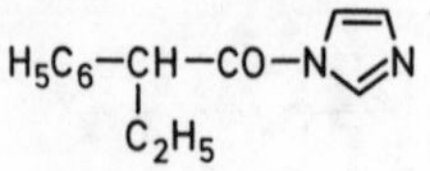

$$H_5C_6-\underset{\underset{C_2H_5}{|}}{CH}-CO-N\overset{\frown}{\underset{\smile}{}}N$$

which is readily prepared by reaction of 2-phenylbutanoic acid with N,N'-carbonyldiimidazole. The reagent reacts with alcohols and amines in benzene.

4.   Experimental Section

4.1.   Reagents and Starting Materials

Directions are given in this section for the conversion of *racemic* 2-phenylbutanoic acid into the corresponding anhydride and acid chloride. Details are then given for the preparation of the same compounds in optically pure form.

racemic 2-Phenylbutanoic acid

The commercial material is cheap and of reasonable purity; it can be distilled, if necessary; b.p. 145–150°/14 mm; m.p. 41°.

racemic 2-Phenylbutanoyl chloride

A slight excess of thionyl chloride is added dropwise to a stirred solution of 2-phenylbutanoic acid in toluene which is cooled in ice-water. The mixture is then heated under reflux for 2–3 hr, the excess of thionyl chloride and the toluene removed by evaporation under reduced pressure, and the product distilled twice under reduced pressure: b.p. 104–106°/15 mm; yield 80%.

racemic 2-Phenylbutanoic anhydride

A mixture of 2-phenylbutanoic acid (100g) and acetic anhydride (100g) is heated under reflux for ∼ 1 hr, at the end of which time the acetic acid produced in the reaction is distilled off slowly. When about 75 g of distillate has been collected, a fresh amount of acetic anhydride is added to the reaction mixture and the process repeated. The same sequence of operations is carried out with a third portion of acetic anhydride, after which acetic acid and anhydride are removed by evaporation under reduced pressure and the 2-phenylbutanoic anhydride is twice purified by distillation under reduced pressure. Yield: 75% (yellow liquid); b.p. 130–155°/0.08 mm, 120–127°/1.5 mm; the color discharges after a few hours.

The yellow coloration of the freshly distilled product is due to the presence of small amounts of ethylphenyl-ketene which is formed, together with 2-phenylbutanoic acid, by thermolysis of the anhydride. These two compounds then react to reform the anhydride, which is thus obtained as a mixture of the *threo* and *erythro* forms. This fact, in turn, explains the rather wide boiling point range of the distillate. The distilled mixture may also contain enolized products such as

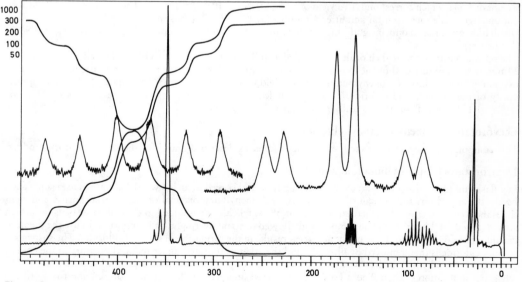

The anhydride thus obtained always contains 3 to 5% of the corresponding acid, the amount of which can readily be estimated by double titration of about 150 mg of the product against N/10 sodium hydroxide. The first titration is carried out in aqueous pyridine and the second in a mixture of pyridine and methanol. The volume of sodium hydroxide which is added in the latter case is normally half of that used in the former titration. The small difference which is found is due to the presence of a little 2-phenylbutanoic acid, and the amount can be calculated.

Examination of the NMR spectrum of the anhydride in benzene-d₆ solution (HA 100 MHz) shows that it consists of essentially equal amounts of the meso and threo diastereoisomers. The signals for both the methyl group triplet and the benzylic proton are well resolved and can be used as internal standards (see Fig. 3)

Figure 3

Dextrorotatory 2-phenylbutanoic acid

A mixture of *racemic* acid (200 g) and cinchonidine (180 g) is heated in a mixture of water (2.1 l) and ethanol (1.4 l) and when all of the solid has dissolved, the mixture is allowed to cool to room temperature. The crystalline salt is filtered and dried to constant weight. Recrystallization from ethanol (750 ml) gives colorless crystals (120 g). The free acid is obtained by shaking a suspension of the salt in $5N$ hydrochloric acid (100 ml) with benzene. Separation and evaporation of the benzene layer gives a liquid (50 g, $\sim 50\%$) with a rotatory power of $[a]_D^{23} = +63.5°$ (neat, $l = 1$). This partially resolved acid is dissolved in pentane and the solution cooled to $-25°$ to crystallize the *racemic* acid. The supernatant liquid is decanted and evaporated to give the liquid acid (37.2 g) with $[a]_D^{23} = +82°$ ($l = 1$), which is suitable for conversion into the anhydride. If acid of very high optical purity is desired, it is prepared as follows via the (–)-1-phenylethylamine salt[14, 15]:

a mixture of the above acid (37 g, $[a]_D^{23} = +82°$) and of optically pure (–)-1-phenylethylamine (27.2 g) in benzene (320 ml) and absolute ethanol (80 ml) is heated to effect solution. The salt which crystallizes on cooling is collected and recrystallized twice from a mixture of benzene (240 ml) and absolute ethanol (60 ml). The acid obtained from this salt as described above (i.e. treatment with hydrochloric acid and benzene) has a rotation after distillation of $[a]_D^{23} = 96.4°$ (neat, $l = 1$); overall yield 25%.

Laevorotatory 2-phenylbutanoic acid

The mother liquors obtained from the first crystallization of the 2-phenylbutanoic acid-cinchonidine salt are enriched with the laevorotatory acid salt. The corresponding free acid can be obtained by acidification and benzene extraction as for the dextrorotatory acid. The crude laevorotatory acid is then dissolved in pentane and separated as before from a large amount of the *racemic* acid. Further resolution of the isolated laevorotatory salt with optically pure (+)-1-phenylethylamine gives laevorotatory 2-phenylbutanoic acid with $[a]_D^{23} = -96.4°$ ($l = 1$, neat).

Dextrorotatory 2-phenylbutanoyl chloride

Oxalyl chloride (3.65 ml, twice the theoretical amount) is added dropwise during 5 min. to a magnetically stirred suspension of dextrorotatory sodium 2-phenylbutanoate (4 g) (from acid of optical purity 96.7%; $[a]_D^{23} = +93.4$ as against $+96.4°$) in anhydrous benzene (30 ml), the temperature being maintained at $0°$ by use of an ice-water bath. There is a vigorous evolution of gas and the suspension becomes less thick as the sodium salt reacts gradually. Stirring is continued at ice bath temperature for 30 min. and then at room temperature overnight, during which time the reaction mixture is protected from atmospheric moisture by a calcium chloride drying tube. At the end of this time there is a copious precipitate of sodium chloride. The reaction mixture is heated at $60°$ in an oil bath for 30 min. and excess oxalyl chloride and benzene are then removed by distillation at atmospheric pressure, the temperature not being allowed to rise above $100°$. Benzene (15 ml) is added to the reaction mixture and removed again by distillation at atmospheric pressure; this process is repeated with further benzene (15 ml). The residual mixture is filtered and the final traces of benzene removed by distillation under reduced pressure. The resulting yellow oil is stored in a dessicator over P_2O_5 to constant weight of 3.54 g which corresponds to a yield of 90%; $[a]_D^{20} = +105°$ ($l = 1$, neat). The crude acid chloride does not undergo facile racemization and after 4 months $[a]_D^{20} = +97.5°$ ($l = 1$, neat).

Distillation gives rise to only insignificant racemization; the fraction with b.p. $119°/22$ mm has $[a]_D^{21} = +96.5°$ ($l = 1$, neat).

The optical purity of the acid chloride is estimated as follows: the chloride (0.598 g) is heated under reflux for 20 min. with a mixture of dioxane (5 ml) and water (0.5 ml). Dilution of the reaction mixture with water and extraction gives colorless 2-phenylbutanoic acid; yield 0.487 g, $[a]_D^{21} = +83°$ (benzene, c = 2.4). The optical purity of the original acid chloride is therefore at least $83 \times 100 = 85\%$ which corresponds to a value of $[a]_D^{21} = +113°$ (liquid) for the optically pure 2-phenylbutanoyl chloride.

Laevorotatory 2-phenylbutanoyl chloride

This compound is prepared in exactly the same manner as described above for the dextrorotatory product.

Dextrorotatory 2-phenylbutanoic anhydride

In a flask equipped with a calcium chloride drying tube and cooled in an ice-water bath are placed some glass beads, the anhydrous sodium salt of dextrorotatory 2-phenylbutanoic acid of high optical purity, and eight times the weight of ether. The theoretical amount of oxalyl chloride is added to the chilled suspension, which is then stirred for 2 hr at room temperature and allowed to stand overnight. (It is important to use the theoretical amount of oxalyl chloride, as use of an excess results in the formation of the acid chloride.) The suspended sodium chloride is then removed by filtration and the ether evaporated under reduced pressure in the cold to give a colorless oil which is dissolved in twice its weight of pentane; the resulting solution is cooled to $-25°$ where crystallization occurs. The crystals are collected and recrystallized from hot pentane to afford the product as needles.

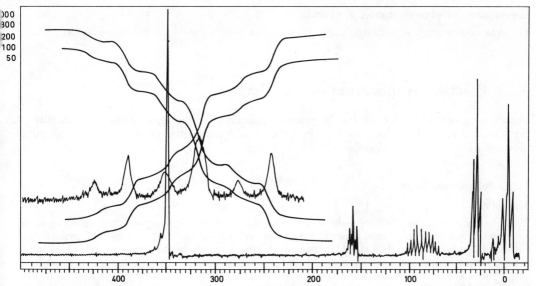

Figure 4

The incompletely purified product is a mixture of the *threo* and *meso* isomers in unequal amounts. The spectrum shown in Fig. 4 obtained from material with an optical purity of 67% clearly shows the difference in the intensity of absorption of the two benzylic proton triplets.

Several more recrystallizations give 2-phenylbutanoic acid anhydride with a rotatory power in the range 145 to 148° [a]. Conversion of a sample of this material into the corresponding acid by heating with aqueous dioxane as in the case of the acid chloride shows that the maximum rotatory power of the anhydride is in fact 150° (the acid obtained in this way has $[a]_D^{21} = 94.4°$, $l = 1$).

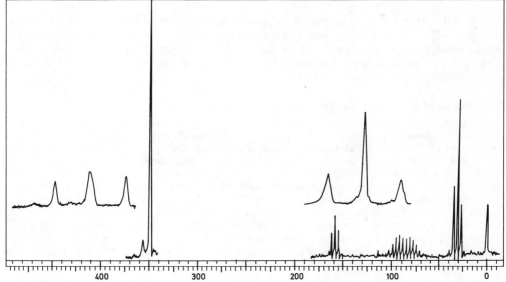

Figure 5

[a] As can be seen from the spectrum shown in Fig. 5, the two triplets are resolved in an anhydride of at least 95% optical purity.

[37] R. Andrisano, A.S. Angeloni, and S. Marzocchi, Tetrahedron **29**, 913 (1973).

[38] B. Rodriguez and S. Valverde, Tetrahedron **29**, 2837 (1973).

Laevorotatory 2-phenylbutanoic anhydride

This compound is prepared in exactly the same manner as described above for the dextrorotatory analog.

4.2.   Practical Application of the Method

Details are given in this section on the practical utilization of the method and on a number of experimental variations which are based on the same fundamental principle. These variations illustrate the scope of the procedure.

4.2.1. Polarimetric Methods

Method A

A weighed amount of the substance under investigation (from a few milligrams to 100 mg, according to the substrate) is added to a solution of about 12.5 % of 2-phenylbutanoic anhydride in anhydrous pyridine. The volume of pyridine solution used should be that which contains twice the theoretical amount of anhydride necessary for esterification. The mixture is allowed to stand at room temperature for several hours, after which time water is added (as much as is compatible with homogeneity). The mixture is left to stand at room temperature for a further 30 min. after which the excess anhydride has been completely hydrolyzed. Benzene and water are then added and the yield of the esterification calculated by titration with base using phenolphthalein as indicator. The aqueous phase is extracted with benzene and acidified, and one of the following two procedures can then be adopted:
– The 2-phenylbutanoic acid produced on acidification of the aqueous phase can be extracted with benzene and the volume of the benzene extracts adjusted such that it is suitable for use in the polarimeter.
– The acid can be obtained by extraction with benzene and evaporation of the solvent. Determination of the rotatory power can then be made either on the crude product or on material purified by distillation. The sense of rotation will yield information on the configuration of the secondary alcohol being examined while the numerical value, taken together with the yield in the esterification, allows the optical yield to be calculated.

Alternatively, no chemical manipulation is required and the course of the reaction can be followed polarimetrically. The rotation of the original mixture varies as esterification proceeds and then in a regular manner as slow racemization of the anhydride takes place which asymptotically tends to a limit. The sign of the acid produced as a result of the resolution can readily be deduced from observations of these changes in rotation.

Determination of the absolute configuration at C-3 in menthol

a) (–)-Menthol (156.7 mg, mw = 156.3) is added to a solution of 2-phenylbutanoic anhydride (620.8 mg, mw = 310) in anhydrous pyridine (5 ml), and the resulting mixture allowed to stand at room temperature for 1 hr. Water ($\sim$ 0.5 ml) is then added to effect hydrolysis, and the mixture left to stand for ½ hr. The organic acid is then titrated against N/10 sodium hydroxide solution in the presence of benzene (5 ml) and a little powdered phenolphthalein (33.10 ml of base are required). The mixture is transferred to a separatory funnel, separated, and the pink aqueous basic phase washed with chloroform to remove traces of menthyl esters and then acidified with 1N hydrochloric acid (3 ml). The 2-phenylbutanoic acid thus formed is extracted with benzene (2 × 5 ml). The benzene extracts are dried over sodium sulfate, filtered, the volume adjusted again to 10 ml and the optical change measured in the polarimeter. Reading at the sodium D line affords +0.524°; consequently, application of the rule in Scheme 2 shows that the carbon atom bearing the hydroxy group has the R configuration. If no menthol was present in the reaction mixture, hydrolysis of the anhydride would give an amount of acid corresponding to

$$N = \frac{620.8 \times 20}{310} = 40.05 \text{ ml of } N/10 \text{ sodium hydroxide solution}$$

If esterification proceeded to completion, the amount of acid consumed would correspond to

$$\frac{156.7 \times 10}{156.26} = 10.03 \text{ ml of } N/10 \text{ sodium hydroxide solution}$$

The yield in the esterification process is therefore

$$\frac{40.05 - 33.10}{10.03} \times 100 = 69.3\%.$$

The theoretical rotation calculated for complete and specific esterification would be

$$\frac{0.1567 \times 164 \times 96.1 \times 1}{156.26 \times 10} = 1.587°.$$

Taking the esterification yield into account, the optical yield is therefore

$$\frac{0.524 \times 100}{1.587 \times 69.3} = 47.6\%$$

In this experiment, in which 2-phenylbutanoic acid was not actually isolated, esterification was allowed to proceed for only 1 hr; consequently, the yield in the esterification was rather low, although readily calculated. The following example, which is typical of the majority of experiments carried out, illustrates the method when esterification is allowed to proceed for 12–20 hr.

β) A mixture of (–)-menthol (153.2 mg) and 2-phenylbutanoic anhydride (607.4 mg) pyridine (5 ml) is allowed to stand at room temperature for 16 hr. After hydrolysis of excess anhydride, it is found that 2.9 ml of 1N sodium hydroxide solution are required to neutralize the 2-phenylbutanoic acid. The volume of 1N sodium hydroxide solution corresponding to the total amount of anhydride is

$$\frac{607.4 \times 2}{310} = 3.91 \text{ ml}$$

and the volume which would have been required had esterification proceeded to completion is given by

$$\frac{153.2}{156.26} = 0.98 \text{ ml}$$

The esterification yield is therefore

$$\frac{3.91 - 2.9}{0.98} \times 100 = 100\%$$

The basic aqueous phase is separated from the organic phase containing the menthyl ester, acidified, and 2-phenylbutanoic acid extracted with benzene. The solvent is removed by evaporation under reduced pressure in a water bath to give 2-phenylbutanoic acid (464 mg). The rotation of a solution of this compound (263.6 mg) in benzene (5 ml) is measured, and

$$[a]_D^{23} = \frac{0.730 \times 5000}{263.6} = 13.9°$$

However, the acid used for this determination is comprised of optically active acid produced during the resolution and of *racemic* acid formed on hydrolysis of the excess *racemic* anhydride in a ratio of 1:2. The optical yield is therefore

$$\frac{13.9 \times 3 \times 100}{96.5} = 43.2\%$$

It should be noted that this value is slightly lower than that obtained in procedure a) above. This is due to the greatly increased time of esterification in the second case, which results in a small amount of racemization of the produced dextrorotatory acid. The isolated acid may also be distilled which sometimes results in a slight increase in rotatory power.

γ) The optical rotation of a pyridine solution of 17β-hydroxy-3-oxoandrostane (0.5 M) and d,l-2-phenyl-butanoic anhydride (1.0 M) is measured in a 1 dm cell; the rotatory power of the reaction solution varies with time as follows:

Time	$[a]_D^{20}$ [°]
0	+4
1 hr	+4.4
1 week	+6.15
15 days	+7

The 2-phenylbutanoic acid which is produced during the kinetic resolution and which is racemized is therefore laevorotatory and the configuration at C-17 must be S (i.e. 17β).

The configuration of 17β-(1-hydroxyethyl)androstane

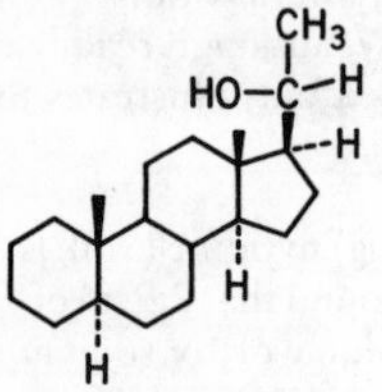

17β-(1-hydroxyethyl)androstane (8.064 mg) is added to a solution of anhydrous pyridine (167 mg) containing 2-phenylbutanoic anhydride (21.9 mg), and the resulting mixture maintained at 0° for 16 hr. A drop of water is added to hydrolyse the excess anhydride (the mixture is allowed to stand for 45 min). The mixture is then transferred to a small dropping funnel together with some benzene and water and titrated against $N/10$ sodium hydroxide using phenolphthalein as indicator. The amount of sodium hydroxide required is 1.28 ml while the amount of anhydride consumed corresponds to 0.13 ml (the theoretical amount for complete esterification is 0.265 ml) and hence the yield in esterification is 49%. The benzene layer is separated and the aqueous layer washed twice with chloroform and then acidified by addition of 1N hydrochloric acid (1 ml). The 2-phenylbutanoic acid is extracted twice with benzene the volume of which is reduced to 1.47 ml (1.240 g). This solution is examined polarimetrically in a 1 dm cell, giving $[a]_D^{23} = +0.038°$; this corresponds to an optical yield of 26%, the hydroxy group studied being in the β-configuration.

Method B

This procedure is based on the large difference in the rotatory power of 2-phenylbutanoic acid in aqueous pyridine and in a mixture of pyridine, water and triethylamine. The following data, which are additional to those listed in Table 1, illustrate this effect:

$[a]_D^{22}$ in pyridine containing 5% water: 107.13°
$[a]_D^{22}$ in pyridine containing 5% water and 10% triethylamine: 24.50°
A pyridine solution which is exactly $M/5$ with respect to the alcohol being investigated and $2M/5$ with respect to 2-phenylbutanoic anhydride is allowed to stand at room temperature for several hours. Water is then added (5% by volume), the mixture allowed to stand for a further 30 min., and the rotation a_1 then measured. Triethylamine (10% by volume) is then added to a portion of this solution and the rotation a_2 read immediately using a 1d cell. (If ($a_1 - 1.1\,a_2$) is positive, then the acid resolved in the esterification reaction will be dextrorotatory, and the configuration of the alcohol can be deduced in the usual manner. If ($a_1 - 1.1\,a_2$) is negative, the acid resolved in the esterification reaction will be laevorotatory. (a_2 is multiplied by 1.1 to allow for the dilution factor on addition of triethylamine and hence to enable the rotations to be compared.)
Division of ($a_1 - 1.1\,a_2$) by 2.6 gives a reasonable approximate value of the optical yield. The value of 2.6 is the result of the following very simple experiment. Water (0.5 ml) is added to an anhydrous pyridine solution (10 ml) which is $M/5$ with respect to both optically pure 2-phenylbutanoic acid and the corresponding *racemic* anhydride and the rotation is read (using a 1 dm cell) after ½ hr (time required for complete hydrolysis of the anhydride); $a_0 = 3.35°$. Triethylamine (0.5 ml) is then added to this solution (5 ml) and the rotation recorded immediately. The value now is $a = 0.70°$. Consequently, $1.1a = 0.77$ and $a_0 = 2.58°$. These values can also be deduced from the values of the rotatory powers given in the various tables.

Examples

An anhydrous pyridine solution $M/5$ in $(+)$-dimethyl tartrate and $2M/5$ in 2-phenylbutanoic anhydride is quickly prepared. The rotations with time are as follows:

Time	$[a]_D^{20} [°]$
5 min	+2.010
10 min	+2.550
1 hr	+3.360
2.5 hr	+3.600
3 hr	+3.630

If water (0.5 ml) is added to this solution, the rotation after ½ hr is 3.550°. Addition of triethylamine (0.5 ml) to the latter solution gives a value of 2.717°. The configuration of the carbon atom is R, since $3.550-(1.1 \times 2.717)$ is positive; the optical yield is $3.550-(1.1 \times 2.717)/2.66 = 22\%$

From the results shown in Table 6 for ten different alcohols, it can be seen that this new procedure compares favorably with the classical method involving extraction of 2-phenylbutanoic acid with either sodium hydroxide or saturated sodium bicarbonate solution. In all cases, the new method gives the expected configuration, and the optical yields obtained are of a satisfactory accuracy.

Table 6: Absolute Configurations of ten different alcohols deduced from the partial resolution method using several prodedures.

| Compound | Conf. of the C-atom studied | | Opt. yield [%] in the resol. | | |
	Found in all cases	Known	Method A	Method B	Method C
$(-)$-menthol	R	R	42.5	44.5	43.5
$(-)$-1-phenylethanol	S	S	45	50	42
2-dimethyl-3-butanol	S	S	37	38	36
17-hydroxy-3-oxoandrostane	S	S	40	42	39[a]
$(-)$-ethyl lactate	S	S	–	38	37
$(-)$-ethyl malate	S	S	–	26	27
$(+)$-dimethyl tartrate	RR	RR	–	22	21
$(+)$-genipine (derivative **25**)	S	–	–	15	–
borjatriol derivative **26**	R	–	–	11.5	–
borjatriol derivative **27**	S	–	–	16[b]	–

Method A: sodium hydroxide   [a] Ref.[9]
     B: triethylamine   [b] Ref.[38]
     C: sodium bicarbonate

Comments

The preceding method offers a number of experimental advantages. In particular, it can be applied to esters which readily undergo hydrolysis such as the tartrates, to compounds which are very water soluble, or to substrates which are highly sensitive to the aqueous basic conditions normally used in the extraction step in the classical method. An example of such a substrate is the hemi-acetal derivative **25** of genipine **24** (Table 6 entry 8). Calculation of the optical yield is based on the assumptions that the molarities of the components and the volumes of the solutions have been exactly adjusted, and that esterification has proceeded to completion. The latter aspect can be checked by following the course of the reaction polarimetrically: the change in rotation as esterification proceeds is frequently followed by a period of no change (which in turn precedes the slow racemization discussed on p. 80).

One further assumption inherent in the use of this method is that the 2-phenylbutanoic ester of the alcohol under study has the same rotatory power in both aqueous pyridine and in aqueous pyridine containing 10% triethylamine. The validity of this assumption has been demonstrated in a number of cases; it is probably unwise, however, to draw similar conclusions in cases where the optical yield is < 10%.

24   25   26   27

4.2.2. The Non-polarimetric Method used in Microdeterminations

The principle of this method[10] outlined p. 56 is based on the premise that if either the dextro- or laevo-rotatory acid is produced in excess (as detected by the rotatory power determined by the above method), then one or the other of the two esters must also be produced in excess.

Determination of the absolute configuration of 1-phenylethanol

a) Q_d–CO–Cl + H_5C_6–CH–CH$_3$
                                                    |
                                                   OH

A solution of the optically pure acid chloride Q_d–CO–Cl (3.65 mg, 2×10^{-5} mol) in carbon tetrachloride (0.02 ml) is added to a solution of 1-phenylethanol (1.22 mg, 10^{-5} mol) in carbon tetrachloride (0.005 ml) contained in a small, ground-glass tube, and the mixture is allowed to stand at room temperature for 18 hr. A drop of either cyclohexanol or aqueous pyridine is then added to destroy the excess anhydride, and the mixture is allowed to stand overnight. A little water is added and the mixture is neutralized with N/10 sodium hydroxide solution. It is then transferred to an ampoule, the aqueous layer is decanted and the organic phase washed twice with water, dried over sodium sulfate, and the solvent evaporated. This gives a mixture of esters (4.3 mg) which is examined by GLC. The retention time of the ester Q_d–COOA$_d$ (peak area 190) is longer than that of the ester Q_d–COOA$_l$ (peak area 106).

β) Q_d–CO–O–CO–Q_l + A_{dl}–OH

A solution of *racemic* anhydride (6.2 mg, 2×10^{-5} mol) in pyridine (0.0125 ml) is added to a solution of 1-phenylethanol in pyridine (0.0125 ml) contained in a small, ground-glass tube, and the mixture allowed is to stand at room temperature for 18 hr. A drop of either methanol or aqueous pyridine is added and the mixture allowed to stand for a further three hr. Several drops of water and benzene are then added, the acid neutralized with N/10 sodium hydroxide solution, and the mixture transferred to an ampoule. The aqueous phase is decanted and the organic layer washed successively with water, 4N hydrochloric acid, water (3 times), dried over sodium sulfate and the solvent evaporated. This gives a mixture of esters (2.5 mg) which is examined by GLC. The retention time of the mixture of esters Q_d–COOA$_l$ + Q_l–COOA$_d$ (peak area 353) is shorter than that of the mixture of esters Q_d–COOA$_d$ + Q_l–COOA$_l$ (peak area 72).

The configuration of the dextrorotatory alcohol is R, and the asymmetric yield, which is identical in value to the optical yield, is given by

$$\frac{353-72}{353+72} \times 100 = 66.1\%$$

The same process can be carried out with dextrorotatory 2,2-dimethyl-3-butanol, but in this case the relative proportions of the esters formed in the reaction are determined by NMR spectrometry.

4.2.3. The Principal Applications of the Method of Partial Resolution. (Summarized in Tables 7–23).

The various examples have been classified in families of compounds. The different variations of the method of partial resolution are also set out in some of the tables.

Table 7: Molecules containing only one asymmetric center located on a chain.

$\underset{\displaystyle |}{OH}$ $H_3C-CH-R$		$\underset{\displaystyle |}{OH}$ $(H_5C_6)_2CH-CH-R$		$\underset{\displaystyle |}{OH}$ $Ar-CH-R$		
R	Ref	R	Ref	Ar	R	Ref.
$-(CH_2)_8-COOCH_3$	39	CH_3	46	C_6H_5	$-CH=CH_2$	43
	40	C_2H_5	46	C_6H_5	$-CH_2-COOCH_3$	44
		C_3H_7	46		$-CH_2-COOCH_3$	44
$-\underset{\displaystyle \underset{CH_3}{|}}{C}=C=CH_2$	41	C_4H_9	46	C_6H_5	$-CH_2-\underset{\displaystyle \underset{CH_2}{\|}}{C}-C_6H_5$	45
$-CH_2-Ar$	42	$CH(CH_3)_2$	46			

Miscellaneous	Ref.
$\underset{\displaystyle |}{OH}$ $HC\equiv C-CH-(CH_2)_4-CH_3$	47
$\underset{\displaystyle |}{OH}$ $H_5C_6-(CH_2)_2-CH-CH_2-CO-CH=CH-C_6H_5$	48
	49

[39] M. Kinoshita, K. Ishii, and S. Umezama, Bull. Chem. Soc. Japan **44**, 3395 (1971).

[40] C.H. Kuo, D. Taub, R.D. Hofsommer, N.L. Wendler, W.H. Urry, and G. Mullenbach, J. Chem. Soc., Chem. Commun. **1967**, 761.

[41] M. Santelli and M. Bertrand, Tetrahedron **30**, 235 (1974).

[42] K. Picker, E. Ritchie, and W.C. Taylor, Aust. J. Chem. **26**, 1111 (1973).

[43] U. Kuffner and K. Schlögl, Monatsh. Chem. **103**, 1320 (1972).

[44] A. Collet and J. Jacques, Bull. Soc. Chim. France **1972**, 3856.

[45] C. Fouquey and J. Jacques, Bull. Soc. Chim. France **1973**, 618.

[46] H.J. Schneider and R. Haller, Tetrahedron **29**, 2509 (1973).

[47] R. Pappo, P. Collins, and C. Jung, Ann. N.Y. Acad. Sci. **180**, 64 (1971).

[48] Y. Asakawa, Bull. Chem. Soc. Japan **45**, 1794 (1972).

[49] E. Fattorusso, L. Minale, G. Sodano, and E. Trivellone, Tetrahedron **27**, 3909 (1971).

[50] H.R. Ansari, Tetrahedron **29**, 1559 (1973).

Table 8: Molecules in which the hydroxy group is located on a chain
bearing several asymmetric centers

$H_3C-\underset{\underset{OH}{|}}{C}H-R$			$Ar-\underset{\underset{OH}{|}}{C}H-R$		
R	Ref.	Ar		R	Ref.
(cyclohexyl with CH₃ and H₃C)	50	C_6H_5		$H_3C-\underset{\underset{C_6H_5}{|}}{\overset{\overset{H_3C}{|}}{C}}-CH-CH_3$	54
(cyclohexyl with H₃C)	51	C_6H_5		$-\underset{\underset{CH_3}{|}}{C}H-COOCH_3$	55
$-CH_2-\overset{O}{\diagdown}-CH(CH_3)_2$	52	$-\bigotimes-CH(CH_3)_2$		(cyclohexanone derivative with H₃C, CH₃, CH₃)	56
$-\underset{\underset{CH_3}{|}}{C}H-CO-\underset{\underset{H_3C}{|}}{C}H-$ (aryl with H₃C, CH₃, OH)	53				
$-CH_2-\underset{\underset{C_2H_5}{|}}{C}H-C_6H_5$	54				

Miscellaneous   Ref.

$H_3C-(CH_2)_{14}-\underset{\underset{COOCH_3}{|}}{\overset{\overset{OH}{|}}{C}}H-CH-(CH_2)_{13}-CH_3$ 57

$H_3C-(CH_2)_{14}-\overset{\overset{OH}{|}}{C}H-CH[(CH_2)_{13}-CH_3]_2$ 57

$H_3C-(CH_2)_3-\overset{\overset{OH}{|}}{C}H$ (pyranone ring with OCH₃)   58

(tricyclic diterpene structure with OCH₃, H₃C, H₃C, CH–CH₃, OH)   59

[51] A. Heymès, M. Dvolaitsky, and J. Jacques, Bull. Soc. Chim. France 1968, 2898.

[52] H. Gerlach and V. Prelog, Justus Liebigs Ann. Chem. 669, 121 (1963).

[53] D.J. Aberhart, K.H. Overton, and S. Huneck, J. Chem. Soc., Chem. Commun. 1969, 162.

[54] M.J. Brienne, C. Oǔannes, and J. Jacques, Bull. Soc. Chim. France 1968, 1036.

[55] J. Canceill, J. Gabard, and J. Jacques, Bull. Soc. Chim. France 1968, 231.

[56] F. Ghozland, Y. Maroni-Barnaud, and P. Maroni, Bull. Soc. Chim. France 1974, 147.

[57] C. Asselineau and J. Asselineau, Bull. Soc. Chim. France 1966, 1992.

[58] G.A. Ellestad, W.J. McGahren, and M.P. Kunstmann, J. Org. Chem. 37, 2045 (1972).

[59] M. Fétizon, G. Moreau, and N. Moreau, Bull. Soc. Chim. France 1969, 1614.

Table 9: Asymmetric center in a 5- or 6- membered ring.

Asymmetric Alcohol	Ref.	Asymmetric Alcohol	Ref.
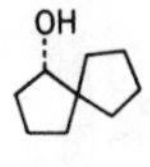	60	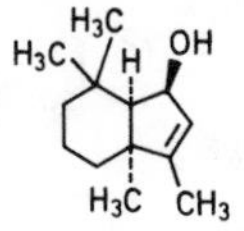	68
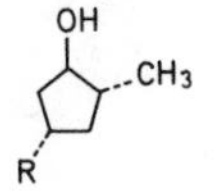	61,62	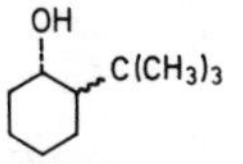	69
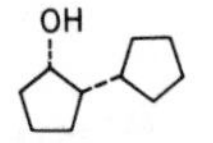	62	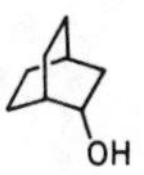	70
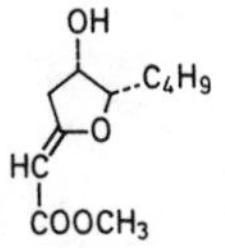	58	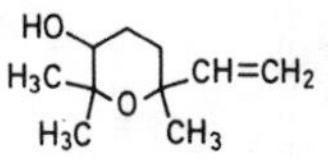	71
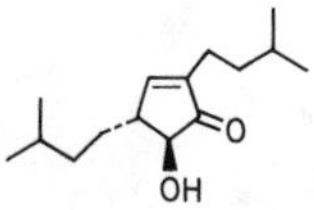	63	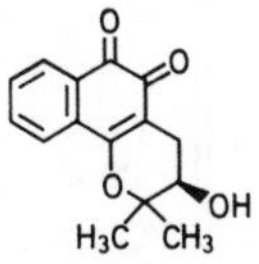	72
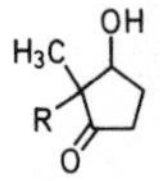	64	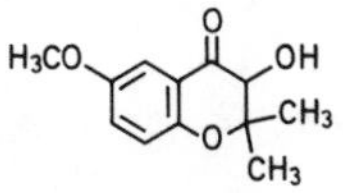	73
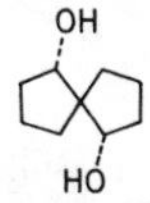	65	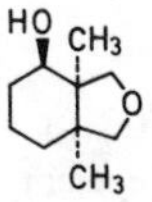	74
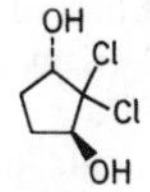	66	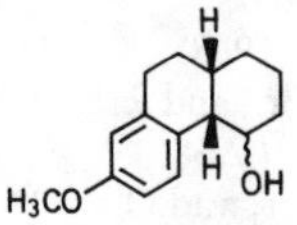	75
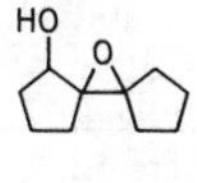	67	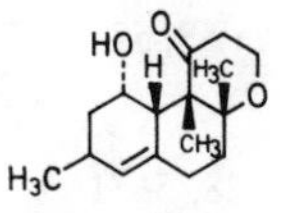	76
		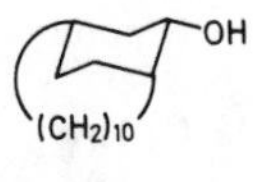	77

[60] H. Christol, D. Duval, and G. Solladié, Bull. Soc. Chim. France 1968, 4151.

[61] D. Varech and J. Jacques, Bull. Soc. Chim. France 1969, 3505.

[62] D. Varech, C. Oŭannes, and J. Jacques, Bull. Soc. Chim. France 1965, 1662.

[63] D. De Keukeleire and M. Verzele, Tetrahedron 27, 4939 (1971).

Table 10: Substituted 1- tetralols and 1-indanols.

Asymmetric Cyclanol	Ref.	Asymmetric Cyclanol	Ref.
R = R' = H	23,24		81
R = CH$_3$; R' = H	22		
R = R' = CH$_3$	21,24		
R = R' = (phthalide ester)	80	R = R' = H	21,24
	23	R = H ; R' = $-CH_2-$ (o-H_3COOC-phenyl)	80
	25	R = R' = (phthalide ester)	80
		R = R' = $\begin{array}{c} COOCH_3 \\ CH_2-C_6H_5 \end{array}$	82
		$H_3COOC-CH_2$, C_6H_5	83

[64] C. Rufer, E. Schröder, and H. Gibian, Justus Liebigs Ann. Chem. **701**, 206 (1967); H. Heidepriem, C. Rufer, H. Kosmol, E. Schröder, and K. Kieslich, Justus Liebigs Ann. Chem. **712**, 155 (1968).

[65] H. Gerlach, Helv. Chim. Acta **51**, 1587 (1968).

[66] S.M. Johnson, I.C. Paul, K.L. Rinehart, Jr., and R. Srinivasan, J. Amer. Chem. Soc. **90**, 136 (1968).

[67] H.J. Wüthrich, A. Siewinski, H. Schaffner, and O. Jeger, Helv. Chim. Acta **56**, 239 (1973).

[68] G. Ohloff and G. Uhde, Helv. Chim. Acta **53**, 531 (1970).

[69] A. Horeau, unpubl. results.

[70] D. Varech and J. Jacques, Tetrahedron **28**, 5671 (1972).

[71] T. Okazaki, A. Ohsuka, and M. Kotake, Nippon Nogei Kagaku Kaishi **2**, 359 (1973).

[72] J. Mock, S.T. Murphy, E. Ritchie, and W.C. Taylor, Austral. J. Chem. **26**, 1121 (1973).

[73] Z. Kis, A. Closse, H.P. Sigg and, L. Hruban, and G. Snatzke, Helv. Chim. Acta **53**, 1577 (1970).

[74] M.G. Peter, G. Snatzke, F. Snatzke, K.N. Nagarajan, and H. Schmid, Helv. Chim. Acta **57**, 32 (1974).

[75] K. Gawecka and S. Meyer, Bull. Acad. Pol. Sci., Ser. Sci. Chim. **21**, 9 (1973).

[76] W.J. McGahren, G.A. Ellestad, J.E. Lancaster, G.O. Morton, and M.P. Kunstmann, J. Amer. Chem. Soc. **96**, 1617 (1974).

[77] H. Heberhardt and K. Schlögl, Justus Liebigs Ann. Chem. **760**, 157 (1972).

[78] P. Bollinger, H.P. Sigg, and H.P. Weber, Helv. Chim. Acta **56**, 819 (1973).

[79] H. Bernotat-Wulf, A. Niggli, L. Ulrich, and H. Schmid, Helv. Chim. Acta **52**, 1165 (1969).

[80] M.J. Luche, A. Marquet, and G. Snatzke, Tetrahedron **28**, 1677 (1972).

[81] Ch. Tamm, B. Böhner, and W. Zürcher, Helv. Chim. Acta **55**, 510 (1972).

[82] H. Falk, W. Fröstl, and K. Schlögl, Tetrahedron Lett. **1974**, 217.

[83] J.H. Brewster and R.T. Prudence, J. Amer. Chem. Soc. **95**, 1217 (1973).

Table 11: Metallocenes.

Asymmetric Alcohol	Ref.	Asymmetric Alcohol	Ref.
	33		88
	84		89
R = CH₃ 36 R = C₂H₅ 85			90
R = H 86 R = CH₃ 87			91

Table 12: Terpenes.

Terpene	Ref.	Terpene	Ref.
(+)-borneol	1		94
isopinocampheol	92		
endonorborneols	5		
(−)-isoborneol	1		95
epiborneol	5		
homoborneol	5		
homoepiborneol	5		
epiisoborneol	5		96
menthol	1		
caranols	93		
genipine derivative	9		

[84] R. Dabard and G. Jaouen, Tetrahedron 39, 3391 (1969).

[85] J. Besançon, G. Tainturier, and J. Tirouflet, Bull. Soc. Chim. France 1971, 1804.

[86] H. Falk and K. Schlögl, Monatsh. Chem. 96, 266 (1965). Contested by D. Marquarding, H. Klusacek, G. Gokel, P. Hoffmann, and I. Ugi, J. Amer. Chem. Soc. 92, 5389 (1970).

[87] G. Haller and K. Schlögl, Monatsh. Chem. 98, 2044 (1967).

[88] P. Dixneuf and R. Dabard, Bull. Soc. Chim. France 1972, 2847.

[89] S.G. Cottis, H. Falk, and K. Schlögl, Tetrahedron Lett. 1965, 2857.

[90] O. Hofer and K. Schlögl, Tetrahedron Lett. 1967, 3485.

Table 13: Sesquiterpenes.

Sesquiterpene	Ref.	Sesquiterpene	Ref.
acoronol[a]	69		101
caryophyllene derivatives	97		
humulene derivatives	98		102
neothujopsanol	99		
ageratriol dimethyl ether	100		103

[a] Optical Yield: 39% (in (−)-2-phenylbutanoic acid)

Table 14: Lactonic sesquiterpenes

Sesquiterpene	Ref.
deacetyl confertiflorin	104
asperilin	105
tamaulipin-B	106, 107
1-epi-allohelenalin	105
dihydrodeacetyl-alloisotenulin	105
dehydroflexuosin A	105
flexuosin B	105
deacetyl-matricarin	108
demathacryl-11-epihexahydrozexbrevin	109
tetraneurin D	110
parthemollin	111
deacetylzeylanine	112
deacetylepitulipinolide	113
dehydroivalbin	114
pycnolide	115
miscellaneous	116, 117, 118, 119

[91] B. Gautheron and R. Broussier, Tetrahedron Lett. 1971, 513.
[92] Y. Chrétien-Bessière, Bull. Soc. Chim. France 1964, 2182.
[93] M.S. Carson, W. Cocker, D.H. Grayson, A.C. Pratt, and P.V.R. Shannon, J. Chem. Soc. [B] 1968, 1136.
[94] W. Cocker, D.P. Hanna, and P.V.R. Shannon, J. Chem. Soc. [C] 1969, 1302.
[95] H. Desalbres, G. Boussac, and Y. Chrétien-Bessière, C.R. Acad. Sci. 268, 1457 (1969).
[96] A.R. Battersby, R.S. Kapil, and R. Southgate, J. Chem. Soc., Chem. Commun. 1968, 131.
[97] A. Horeau and J.K. Sutherland, J. Chem. Soc. [C] 1966, 247.
[98] N.P. Damodaran and Sukh Dev, Tetrahedron 24, 4133 (1968).
[99] S.P. Acharya and H.C. Brown, J. Org. Chem. 35, 3874 (1970).
[100] R. Grandi, A. Marchesini, U.M. Pagnoni, R. Tran, and L. Garanti, Tetrahedron 30, 3821 (1974).
[101] H. Nagano, Y. Tanahashi, Y. Moriyama, and T. Takahashi, Bull. Chem. Soc. Japan 46, 2840 (1973).

Table 15: Di- and triterpenes

Terpene	Ref.
α-amyrin	1
β-amyrin	3
$(-)$-β-lanosterol[a]	69
hopanol	120
aglaiol derivative	121
3β-acetoxy-24-hydroxy-5α-lanost-8-ene	122
miscellaneous	123, 124
trachylobanic acid methyl ester	125
deacetyl zanzibaric acid methyl ester	126
grayanotoxin	127, 128
isofoliol acetonide	129
borjatriol derivatives	38

[a] optical yield: 43%

[102] P. Teisseire, M. Plattier, Wojnarowski, and G. Ourisson, Bull. Soc. Chim. France 1966, 2749.

[103] J. Streith, P. Pesnelle, and G. Ourisson, Bull. Soc. Chim. France 1963, 518.

[104] N.H. Fisher and T.J. Mabry, Tetrahedron 23, 2529 (1967).

[105] W. Herz and H.B. Kagan, J. Org. Chem. 32, 216 (1967).

[106] N.H. Fisher and T.J. Mabry, J. Chem. Soc., Chem. Commun. 1967, 1235.

[107] H. Yoshioka, W. Renold, N.H. Fisher, A. Higo, and T.J. Mabry, Phytochemistry 9, 823 (1970).

[108] E.H. White, S.E. Guchi, and J.N. Marx, Tetrahedron 25, 2099 (1969).

[109] A.R. de Vivar, C. Guerrero, E. Diaz, and A. Ortega, Tetrahedron 26, 1657 (1970).

[110] H. Yoshioka, H. Rüesch, E. Rodriguez, A. Higo, J.A. Mears, T.J. Mabry, J.G. Calzada, A. and X.A. Dominguez, Tetrahedron 26, 2167 (1970).

[111] W. Herz, S.V. Bhat, and A.L. Hall, J. Org. Chem. 35, 1110 (1970).

[112] K. Takeda, I. Horibe, M. Teraoka, and H. Minato, J. Chem. Soc. [C] 1970, 973.

[113] R.W. Doskotch, F.S. El-Feraly, J. Org. Chem. 35, 1928 (1970).

[114] H. Chikamatsu and W. Herz, J. Org. Chem. 38, 585 (1973).

[115] W. Herz and R.P. Sharma, J. Org. Chem. 40, 392 (1975).

[116] H. Yoshioka, A. Higo, and T.J. Mabry, Phytochemistry 10, 401 (1971).

[117] H.P. Weber, D. Hauser, and H.P. Sigg, Helv. Chim. Acta 54, 2763 (1971).

[118] A. Yoshitake and T.A. Geissman, Phytochemistry 8, 1753 (1969).

[119] R.W. Doskotch, F.S. El-Feraly, and C.D. Hufford, Canad. J. Chem. 49, 2103 (1971).

[120] G. Berti, F. Bottari, A. Marsili, and I. Morelli, Tetrahedron Lett. 1968, 529.

[121] R.B. Boar and M.K. Damps, J. Chem. Soc., Chem. Commun. 4, 115(1973).

[122] R.B. Boar, D.A. Lewis, and J.F. McGbie, J. Chem. Soc., Perkin Trans. 1, 2231 (1972).

[123] J.F. Biellmann, Tetrahedron Lett. 1966, 4803.

[124] G. Piancatelli, S. Corsano, and A. Scettri, Gazz. Chim. Ital. 101, 797 (1971).

[125] G. Hugel, L. Lods, J.M. Mellor, D.W. Theobald, and G. Ourisson, Bull. Soc. Chim. France 1965, 2888.

[126] G. Hugel and G. Ourisson, Bull. Soc. Chim. France 1965, 2903.

[127] Z. Kumazawa and R. Iriye, Tetrahedron Lett. 1970, 931.

[128] T. Matsumoto and M. Watanabe, Tetrahedron Lett. 1968, 6019.

Table 16: Steroids

Steroid	Ref.
3β-hydroxy-4-substituted steroids	[3]
3β-hydroxy-2α-methyl-5α-cholestane[a]	[69]
3α-hydroxy-2α-methyl-5α-cholestane[b]	[69]
17β-benzoyloxy-2α-bromo-3β-hydroxy-5α-androstane[c]	[69]
17β-benzoyloxy-2α-bromo-3α-hydroxy-5α-androstane[d]	[69]
4α-hydroxy-A-nor-5β-cholestane	[130]
6α- and 6β-hydroxy steroids	[3]
6β-hydroxy-5α-androstane	[131]
4,4-dimethyl-6α-hydroxy-5α-androstane	[132]
11α-hydroxy steroids	[3]
11α-hydroxy-3,17-dioxo-10α-androst-4-ene	[133]
3β,12α-diacetoxy-11β-hydroxy-17α-pregnane	[134]
12α-hydroxy steroids	[3]
17β-hydroxy steroids	[1, 3]
17β-hydroxy-3-oxo-D-nor-androst-4-ene	[3]
17α-hydroxy steroids	[1, 3]
17α-hydroxy-13α-androstane	[135]
17α-hydroxy-3-oxo-14β-androst-4-ene	[136]
20β-hydroxy steroids	[1, 3]
20α-hydroxy steroids	[1, 3]
3β-benzoyloxy-20-hydroxy-4-oxocholestane	[137]

R = C$_2$H$_5$; R' = H	[138]
R = H ; R' = OCH$_3$	[139]

[a] optical yield: 32% in (+)-2-phenylbutanoic acid.
[b] optical yield: 8% in (−)-2-phenylbutanoic acid.
[c] optical yield: 63% in (+)-2-phenylbutanoic acid.
[d] optical yield: 27% in (−)-2-phenylbutanoic acid.

[129] T. Ga de Quesada, B. Rodriguez, S. Valverde, and S. Huneck, Tetrahedron Lett. 1972, 2187.

[130] I. Morelli, S. Catalano, G. Moretto, and A. Marsili, Tetrahedron Lett. 1972, 717.

[131] M. Fétizon, M. Golfier, and J. Rens, Ann. Chim. (Paris) 8, 161 (1973).

[132] M. Fétizon and P. Foy, Bull. Soc. Chim. France 1967, 2653.

[133] G. Saucy, M. Müller, and A. Fürst, Helv. Chim. Acta 50, 1394 (1967).

[134] T. Tschesche and H. Muller-Albrecht, Chem. Ber. 103, 350 (1970).

[135] M. Fétizon and J.C. Gramain, Bull. Soc. Chim. France 1967, 1003.

[136] P. Crabbe, A. Cruz, and J. Iriarte, Canad. J. Chem. 46, 349 (1968).

[137] E.P. Burrows, G.M. Hornby, and E. Caspi, J. Org. Chem. 34, 103 (1969).

[138] W. Sucrow, B. Schubert, W. Richter, and M. Slopianka, Chem. Ber. 104, 3689 (1971).

[139] H. Chwastek, N. Le Goff, R. Epsztein, and M. Baran-Marszak, Tetrahedron 30, 603 (1974).

Table 17: Alkaloids

Alkaloid	Optical yield (%) and sign[a]		Ref.
N-methylephedrin	21	(−)	69
ribalidinin			140

$$H_5C_6-\underset{\underset{OH}{|}}{CH}-CH_2-\underset{\underset{R}{|}}{CH}-N(CH_3)_2$$

R = H			33
R = C_6H_5			46

$$H_5C_6-\underset{\underset{OH}{|}}{CH}-\underset{\underset{CH_3}{|}}{CH}-CH_2-N(CH_3)_2 \qquad 141$$

quinine	51	(−)	69
pendamine	36	(−)	69
codeine			1
cassaine	34	(+)	69
prosafrine	21	(+)	69
isoprosopinine	38	(−)	69
dihydrominovincin			142
phomine and dehydrophomine			143
prosopine			144
prosopinine			144
chlorophyll α-derivative			145

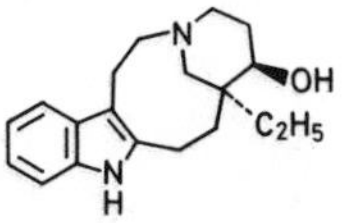

146

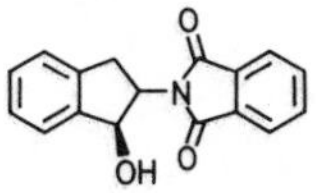

80

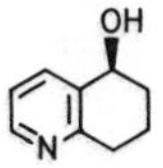

147

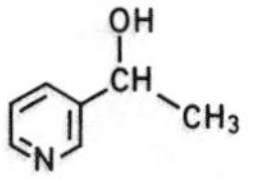

147

[a] of 2-phenylbutanoic acid. Absolute configuration of alcaloids deduced from scheme 2 (p. 54) are in agreement with known configuration

[140] J.P. Guetté and N. Spassky, Bull. Soc. Chim. France 1972, 4217.

[141] L. Angliolini and G. Gottarelli, Tetrahedron 26, 421 (1970).

[142] W. Döpke and H. Meisel, Tetrahedron Lett. 1970, 749.

[143] W. Rothweiler and Ch. Tamm, Helv. Chim. Acta 53, 696 (1970).

[144] Q. Khuong-Huu, G. Ratle, X. Monseur, and R. Goutarel, Bull. Soc. Chim. Belg. 81, 425 (1972).

[145] H. Brockmann and J. Bode, Justus Liebigs Ann. Chem. 1974, 1017.

[146] J.J. Dugan, M. Hesse, U. Renner, and H. Schmid, Helv. Chim. Acta 9, 60 (1967).

[147] G. Gottarelli and B. Samori, Tetrahedron Lett. 1970, 2055.

Table 18: Chirality due to deuterium substitution

	Ref.
R—CH—D | OH R = C(CH$_3$)$_3$, n-C$_3$H$_7$, n-C$_5$H$_{13}$	4
OH | CD$_3$—CH—CH$_3$	13

Table 19: 1,2-Diols

1,2-Diol	Ref.
OH | R—CH—CH$_2$OH	140

OH CH$_3$
| |
HO—CH$_2$—CH—C—(CH$_2$)$_2$—OH
      |
      CH$_3$
	21

OH OH | | H$_5$C$_6$—CH—CH—C$_6$H$_5$	140
ambrosiol	148
20,22-dihydroxycholestane[a]	69
3β-acetoxy-20,22-dihydroxycholest-4-ene	149
14β,15β-dihydroxy-4,4-dimethylandrostane[b]	69
14a,15a-dihydroxy-4,4-dimethylandrostane[c]	69
17a,20a-dihydroxy-3β-methoxy-21-methyl-17a-pregn-4-ene	139
5a,6a-dihydroxy steroids	131
austdiol	150
2,3-dihydroxysqualene	151
24,25-dihydroxycholesterol derivatives	64

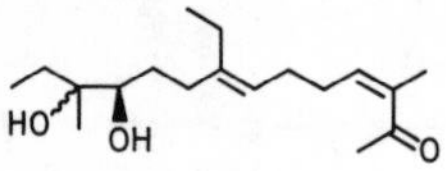	152

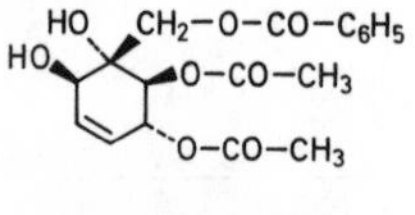	153

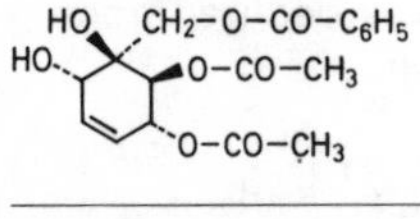	153

[a] optical yield: 14% in (−)-2-phenylbutanoic acid
[b] optical yield: 20% in (−)-2-phenylbutanoic acid
[c] optical yield: 67% in (+)-2-phenylbutanoic acid

[148] T.J. Mabry, W. Renold, H.E. Miller, and H.B. Kagan, J. Org. Chem. **31**, 681 (1966).

[149] N.K. Chaudhuri, R. Nickolson, H. Kimball, and M. Gut, Steroids, **15**, 525 (1970).

Table 20: α-Hydroxy esters

$R-CHOH-COOCH_3$	
$R = CH_3, -CH_2-CH(CH_3)_2, C(CH_3)_3$:	Ref.[140]
methyl 23-hydroxycholanoate:	Ref.[154]
$H_5C_2-CHOH-P(OCH_3)_2$:	Ref.[155]
$\quad\quad\quad\quad\quad\quad\quad\overset{\|}{O}$	

Table 21: Secondary alcohols with equal branching at carbon atoms close to the asymmetric center

Secondary alcohol	Optical yield (%)		Ref.
3β-hydroxy-17-oxoandrostane	7	a	[69]
3β-hydroxy-17-oxo-19-norandrostane	2.2	a	[69]
3α-hydroxy-17-oxo-5β-androstane	4.4	b	[69]
hecogenine	10	a	[69]
dehydroruscogenine	6	a	[69]
3β-hydroxy-17-oxoandrost-4-ene	1.8	a	[20]
			[156]
α-D-glucofuranose diacetonide	54	a	[157]
α-D-alloglucofuranose diacetonide	21	a	[157]
helenaline			[105]
cis- and trans-khellactone methyl ether			[79]
tetrahydrohelenaline			[105]
dihydromexicanine			[105]

a: (+)-2-phenylbutanoic acid
b: (−)-2-phenylbutanoic acid

[150] R. Vleggaar, P.S. Steyn, and D.W. Nagel, J. Chem. Soc., Perkin Trans. 1, 45 (1974).

[151] R.B. Boar and K. Damps, Tetrahedron Lett. 1974, 3731.

[152] A.S. Meyer, E. Hanzmann, and R.C. Murphy, Proc. Nat. Acad. Sci. USA 68, 2312 (1971).

[153] R.B. Boar and K. Damps, Tetrahedron Lett. 1974, 3731; R. Hollands, D. Becker, A. Gaudemer, and J. Polonsky, Tetrahedron 24, 1633 (1968).

[154] Y. Yanuka, R. Katz, and S. Sarel, Tetrahedron Lett. 1970, 5229.

[155] N.N. Girotra and N.L. Wendler, Tetrahedron Lett. 1969, 4647.

[156] G. Gimino, S. De Stefano, L. Minale, and E. Fattorusso, Tetrahedron 27, 4673 (1971).

[157] W. Renold (unpubl. results).

[158] J.P. Guetté, M. Perlat, J. Capillon, and D. Boucherot, Tetrahedron Lett. 1974, 2411.

[159] J. Paul and K. Schlögl, Monatsh. Chem. 104, 274 (1973).

[160] C.J.W. Brooks and J.D. Gilbert, J. Chem. Soc., Chem. Commun. 1973, 194.

[161] J.D. Gilbert and C.J.W. Brooks, Anal. Lett. 6, 639 (1973).

[162] M. Seki, N. Koizumi, M. Morisaki, and N. Ikekawa, Tetrahedron Lett. 1975, 15.

[163] S. Hagishita and K. Kuriyama, Tetrahedron 28, 1435 (1972).

Table 22: Absolute configuration of the enantiomers of a *racemic* alcohol using optically active 2-phenylbutanoic anhydride

Secondary Alcohol	Ref.
$\overset{\displaystyle OH}{\underset{\displaystyle |}{R-CH-CH_3}}$ R = C_2H_5, $CH(CH_3)_2$, $CH_2-CH(CH_3)_2$, $C(CH_3)_3$, $CH_2-C_6H_5$, $(CH_2)_8-CH_3$	8
$\overset{\displaystyle OH}{\underset{\displaystyle |}{R-CH-C_6H_5}}$ R = CH_3, C_2H_5, C_3H_7, $CH(CH_3)_2$, C_4H_9, $CH_2-CH(CH_3)_2$, $C(CH_3)_3$, C_6H_{11}	8
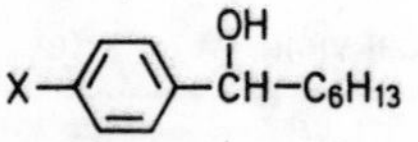 $X-\langle\text{C}_6\text{H}_4\rangle-\overset{\displaystyle OH}{\underset{\displaystyle |}{CH}}-C_6H_{13}$ X = CH_3, OCH_3, CF_3	158
menthol	8
$\overset{\displaystyle OH}{\underset{\displaystyle |}{H_5C_2-CH-CH_2-CH(CH_3)_2}}$	8
HO— (fused ring structure)	43
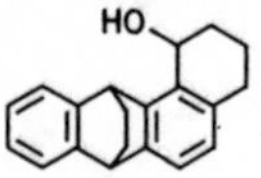 HO— (fused ring structure)	159

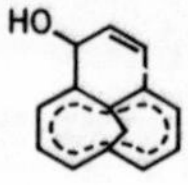

Table 23: Non-polarimetric methods which can be used in microdeterminations[10]

NMR-modification	VPC-modification
$(H_3C)_3C-CHOH-CH_3$	$H_5C_6-CHOH-CH_3$
(steroid structure with H_3C, OH, H, H_3CO)	$H_5C_6-CHOH-C_4H_9$
	(−)-menthol

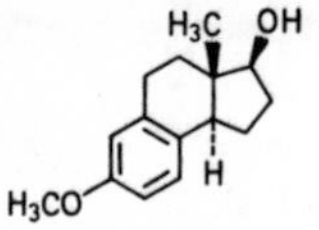

For another VPC modification of Horeau's method see Ref.[160–162]:
A chiral amine which reacts rapidly with the excess 2-phenylbutanoic anhydride is added to the reaction mixture and the diastereoisomeric amides formed are estimated by VPC. One should be cautions about assigning the absolute configurations.

Determination of the absolute configuration of an acid by kinetic resolution with a secondary alcohol:

d,l-anhydrides and (−)-menthol	Ref. [33]
optically active acid chloride and *d,l*-1-phenylethanol	Ref. [163]

Determination of Absolute Configurations of Organic Compounds by Asymmetric Synthesis, by Resolution, and by Enzymatic Methods

J.C. Fiaud

Laboratoire de Synthèse Asymétrique, Université de Paris-Sud, Orsay, France.

Table of Contents

1. Introduction

There are two distinct chemical methods which can be used for the determination of the absolute configuration of chiral centres in organic molecules:
(a) direct correlation, in which the compound of unknown configuration is transformed into a product of known configuration (or vice versa) by chemical reactions which do not in any way modify the nature of the element of asymmetry.
(b) Correlation by asymmetric synthesis, in which the compound of unknown configuration is involved in one reaction of an asymmetric synthesis, either as substrate, reagent or product. The reaction involves the diastereoisomeric transition states.

Three types of reaction can be distinguished:
(a) Treatment of a prochiral substrate A with an optically active reagent B* results in the formation of an optically active product C*. For a series of similar compounds A, the configuration of C* can be related to the configuration of the reagent B* by a stereochemical model which describes the steric course of the reaction:

$$A_{prochiral} + B^* \longrightarrow C^*$$

Most of the reactions of this type involve reductions by means of chiral compounds such as hydrides complexed by sugars or by alcohols and amino alcohols, chiral boranes, chiral Grignard reagents, magnesium and aluminum alcoholates, etc. The prochiral substrates A are olefins, aldehydes, ketones, or imines.

(β) Reaction of a symmetric reagent B with an asymmetric compound which contains the prochiral group A results in the formation of the diastereoisomers Z*–C*:

$$Z^*-A_{prochiral} + B \longrightarrow \underset{\text{diastereoisomers}}{Z^*-C^*} \longrightarrow \underset{\text{enantiomers}}{C^*}$$

The configuration of the new element of asymmetry which has been thus created, C*, can frequently be related to the configuration of the element of asymmetry originally present, Z*, by means of a stereochemical model. It is thus the relative configuration of the second element of asymmetry C* which is determined by comparison with that of the first, Z*.

The subsequent discussion is limited to those cases in which the substrate is chiral at one position, and where the product obtained can be readily transformed into a mixture of enantiomers, i.e. where the inducing chiral center is eliminated or destroyed. This definition includes those reactions which involve transformation of one element of chirality into another element of chirality, generally by a rearrangement or an elimination reaction. If the stereochemistry of the reaction is known it is then possible to deduce the absolute configuration of one element from a knowledge of that of the other one and with the assistance of a stereochemical model.

(γ) Kinetic resolution reactions of a racemic substance with an optically active reagent allow determination of configuration in cases where the configuration of the reagent can be correlated with the configuration of the more reactive enantiomer of the substrate.

In general terms, therefore, the determination of configuration is based on the concept of a stereochemical model which suitably describes the stereochemical course of the reaction. The model is chosen such that it can account for the stereochemistry of a reaction carried out with a series of compounds of known configuration, and attempts are often made to select models which represent the more favored diastereoisomeric transition state with respect to the steric and electronic interactions between non-bonded atoms. The model is also often semi-empirical. Such a model, which is valid for a series of compounds of known configuration, can then be used for the determination of configuration of other compounds, provided that the latter have structures similar to those of the compounds used in the construction of the model, and that the same types of interactions are operative in the two types of substrates.

The most reliable asymmetric syntheses are those which proceed with high stereoselectivity. The correct selection of the preferred diastereoisomeric transition state is easier the higher the stereo-

selectivity of the reaction involving the asymmetric synthesis. There are two criteria by which the quality of a method for the determination of absolute configuration by asymmetric synthesis may be judged:
(a) the number of examples of known configuration on which the stereochemical model is based
(b) the values of the stereoselectivities generally obtained in these syntheses.
The determination of absolute configuration of secondary alcohols by asymmetric atrolactic synthesis (Prelog's method) and by kinetic resolution with 2-phenylbutanoic acid (Horeau's method) have been treated elsewhere.

2.　Asymmetric Reduction of Prochiral Substances by Optically Active Reagents

Many methods for the determination of absolute configuration involve asymmetric reduction of olefins, aldehydes, ketones, or imines by chiral reagents. The asymmetric synthesis proceeds via hydride transfer from the chiral reagent 2 to the achiral substrate 1.

The configuration of the resulting alkanes, alcohols or amines 3 can be correlated with the configuration of the reducing agent, provided that the steric course of the reaction is known. This is normally the case, the steric course of the reduction having been previously elucidated from the results of reactions carried out with prochiral substrates to give products of known configuration. The reducing agents which have been employed in such asymmetric syntheses fall into three groups:
(a) chiral complexes of hydrogenation catalysts;
(b) chiral complexes of hydrides of lithium, aluminum and borane;
(c) chiral reducing agents in which the hydride is transferred from a carbon atom, such as reducing Grignard reagents and alcoholates of aluminum and magnesium.

2.1.　Hydrogenation in the Presence of Chiral Complexes as Catalysts

Catalytic hydrogenation of a number of a-substituted styrenes under homogeneous conditions has been studied[1]. The catalyst was prepared in situ by treatment of $(RhCl-1,5-hexadiene)_2$ with a chiral tertiary phosphine 4, Horner has shown that there is a relationship between the absolute configuration of the chiral phosphine and that of the hydrogenation product 5. This relationship can readily be seen from the model of asymmetric induction 6. The tetrahedral complex is constructed such that the two phosphine ligands are situated on one side of the octahedron and

their conformations are such that the large phenyl groups are as far apart as possible. Cis addition of hydrogen to the styrene thus leads to the alkane 5. The results obtained from reactions of this type are summarized in Table 1.

Table 1: Configuration of alkanes obtained by catalytic hydrogenation of olefins[1]

X	Configuration	Optical purity (e.e. %)	Configuration and observed $[\alpha]_D^{(0)}$						
			C₂H₅	C₃H₇	α-benzyl	α-naphthyl	CH₃O	C₂H₅O	2-phenylbutane
C₃H₇	R (−)	100	R (−) 7.7	R (−) 8.9	R (−) 6.85	R (+) 1.6	S (−) 3.0	S (−) 2.7	S (+) 5.1
	S (+)	90	S (+) 7.1	S (+) 7.4	S (+) 6.2	S (−) 0.8	R (+) 3.0	R (+) 2.7	R (−) 6.6
C₄H₉	R (−)	100	R (−) 7.5	R (−) 7.7			S (−) 2.7	S (−) 2.6	
	S (+)	80	S (+) 6.3	S (+) 1.8			R (+) 2.1	R (+) 2.1	
CH(CH₃)₂	S (−)	100	S (+) 17.4	R (−) 1.5			R (+) 0.5	R (+) 0.9	
C(CH₃)₃	R (+)	10	R (−) 1.1						

Reactions are generally carried out with 10^{-2} mol of α-substituted styrene, 0.5×10^{-4} mol of μ-dichloro-bis-(1,5-hexadiene-rhodium) and 3.0×10^{-4} mol of phosphine in benzene (20 ml) at 30°C.

Experimental[1]

Under thermostatically controlled conditions and by use of a closed system, μ-dichloro-bis-(1,5-hexadiene-rhodium) is dissolved in benzene (20 ml) under a hydrogen atmosphere. Optically active phosphine (3×10^{-4} mol) is injected into the solution, whereupon the color changes within a few seconds from yellow to brown-red, and then reverts to yellow-orange. The styrene is then added and the reaction mixture stirred for 1–2 hr. The optically active alkane is isolated from the reaction mixture by column chromatography.

2.2.　Reduction by Chiral Hydride Complexes

2.2.1. Landor's Method

Complexes prepared by reaction of lithium aluminum hydride with derivatives of monosaccharides have been utilized as chiral reagents for the reduction of ketones. Initial investigation of the complexes derived from a variety of sugars revealed low stereoselectivities in the asymmetric syntheses[2]; it was however subsequently shown that the reagent prepared by reaction of equivalent amounts of lithium aluminum hydride with 3-O-benzyl-1,2-O,O-cyclohexylidene-a-D-glucofuranoside (7) reduced ketones with stereoselectivities as high as 45% in some cases. Nine different ketones were reduced with this reagent (Table 2); in each case, the

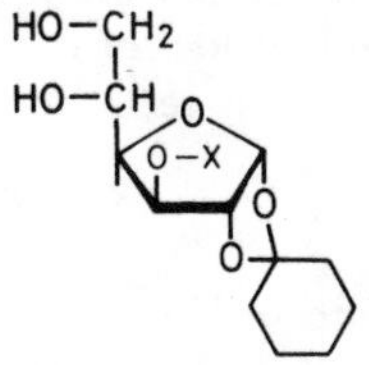

HO—CH$_2$
HO—CH O
O—X
O
O

X = CH$_2$—C$_6$H$_5$

7

corresponding secondary alcohol of S-configuration was obtained with good stereoselectivity.

Table 2:　Asymmetric ketone reduction using the LiAlH$_4$-**7** complex[3]

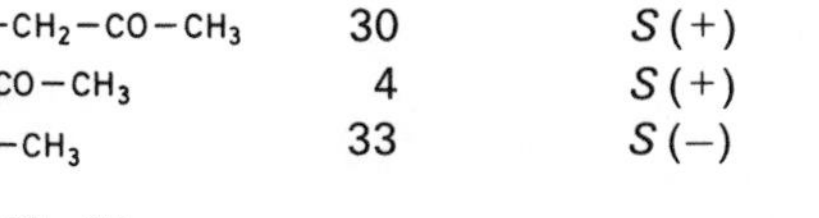

$$R-\underset{O}{\overset{\|}{C}}-R' \xrightarrow{\text{LiAlH}_2 \text{(OR}^*)_2} R-\underset{OH}{\overset{H}{\underset{|}{\overset{|}{C}}}}-R'$$

8　　　　　　　　　　　　　　　　　　　**9**

	e.e. (%)	configuration	yield %
(H$_3$C)$_2$CH—CH$_2$—CO—CH$_3$	30	S (+)	66
(H$_3$C)$_3$C—CO—CH$_3$	4	S (+)	55–61
H$_5$C$_6$—CO—CH$_3$	33	S (−)	75–83
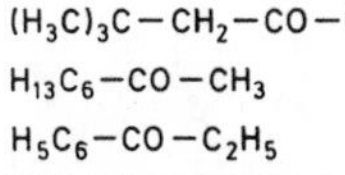 CO—CH$_3$ (naphthyl)	29	S (−)	86
(H$_3$C)$_2$C=CH—CO—CH$_3$	30	S (+)	61–86
H$_9$C$_4$—CO—CH$_3$	11	S (+)	70
(H$_3$C)$_3$C—CH$_2$—CO—CH$_3$	15	S (+)	84
H$_{13}$C$_6$—CO—CH$_3$	11	S (+)	83
H$_5$C$_6$—CO—C$_2$H$_5$	38	S (−)	73–81

The results were interpreted on the basis of a cyclic complex formed by interaction of lithium aluminum hydride with the hydroxy groups at C-5 and C-6 in the sugar molecule. Examination of a molecular model of such a complex 10 reveals that, of the two remaining hydrogen atoms bound

10   11

to aluminum, H^1 is considerably more shielded by the benzyl group than H^2. According to the hypothesis of Landor, the favored transition state is that in which the carbonyl group of the ketone is directed away from the oxygen atoms in the sugar molecule, and that the disposition of the groups R_M and R_L in the ketone are such that steric interactions between the ketone and the complex are at a minimum. This means, the larger of the two groups should be oriented opposite to the "3-O-benzyl shielding group". Consequently, reduction of ketone should proceed via preferential transfer of the hydrogen atom H^2 to afford the alcohol with the configuration 11.

It is essential to use standardized, titrated solutions of lithium aluminum hydride for the preparation of the reagent[4], and the ratio of reagents $LiAlH_4$:sugar:ketone = 1:1:1 is recommended for maximum stereoselectivity.

Preparation of a titrated solution of lithium aluminum hydride

Lithium aluminum hydride (10 g) is stirred with ether (400 ml) at room temperature for 2 hr, and the resulting mixture filtered through a sintered glass funnel (the solid residue ignites on exposure to air or on decomposition with alcohol). The filtered solution is standardized by addition of a four-fold excess of a standard solution of iodine in sodium-dried benzene followed by titration of the excess iodine with sodium thiosulfate.

Reduction of ketones with the $LiAlH_4$-3-O-benzyl-1,2-O-cyclohexylidene-a-glucofuranose complex formed with a standardized solution of $LiAlH_4$.

The furanose (8.8 g, 0.025 mol) in dry ether (50 ml) is added to a measured volume of a standardized ether solution of the hydride containing ca. 20–23 g/l. The mixture is heated under reflux for 30 min., and the ketone (0.025 mol) in dry ether (50 ml) then added. After a further 2 hr heating under reflux, the mixture is cooled, water (15 ml) cautiously added, and the precipitated hydroxides filtered off on kielselguhr. The secondary alcohol 11 is isolated from the ethereal solution by distillation, and the purity checked by G.L.C.

Experimental evidence has also been provided to support the hypothesis that H^2 in model 10 is indeed preferentially transferred to the ketone during reduction. Thus, addition of one equivalent of ethanol to the $LiAlH_4$-sugar complex results in the formation of the alkoxy complex 12 formed by removal of the more accessible H^2 hydrogen. Subsequent reduction of ketones with this new reducing agent affords alcohols 13 which exhibit the opposite configuration compared with those previously obtained with the complex 10 via transfer of H^1 during reduction (see Table 3)[5].

12   13

Table 3: Reduction of ketones using a standardized ethereal solution of $LiAlH_4$ for the preparation of the monosaccharide derivative complex prior to modification with ethanol[5, a].

Ketone	mmol	$LiAlH_4$ (mmol)	Ethanol (mmol)	Alcohol e.e. (%)	Alcohol config.	Alcohol yield (%)
$H_5C_6-CO-CH_3$	12.5	26	39	59	R	60–80
$H_5C_6-CO-C_2H_5$	13	25	33	39	R	60–80
$H_7C_3-CO-CH_3$	20	25	28	10	R	
$(H_3C)_2CH-CH_2-CO-CH_3$	20	25	28	13	R	
$(H_3C)_3C-CH_2-CO-CH_3$	13	40	98	4.4	R	
(naphthyl) $CO-CH_3$	13	35	35	40	R [b]	
$H_{13}C_6-CO-CH_3$	13	40	98	25	R	

[a] monosaccharide derivative 25 mmol.
[b] first determination of configuration.

Reduction of ketones with the ethanol modified $LiAlH_4$ complex of 3-O-benzyl-1,2-O-cyclohexylidene-a-D-glucofuranose, prepared form a standardized etheral solution of $LiAlH_4$

A solution of 3-O-benzyl-1,2-O-cyclohexylidene-a-D-glucofuranose (8.8 g, 0.025 mol) in dry ether is added dropwise to a standard ethereal solution of $LiAlH_4$ (0.025 M). The mixture is heated under reflux for 40 min. before dropwise addition of a solution of ethanol (3.0 g, 0.065 mol) in ether (50 ml) followed (after 1 hr) by the addition of a solution of the ketone (0.0125 mol) in dry ether (50 ml). After a two-hour period of heating, the mixture is cooled, water (15 ml) added, and the precipitated hydroxides removed by filtration. The product is isolated as described above.

As a result of the very precise experimental conditions under which these reactions are conducted (filtered solutions of $LiAlH_4$, rigorous stoichiometry), Landor's method satisfies the criteria necessary in a suitable chemical method for the determination of absolute configuration by asymmetric synthesis. The reactions, which are carried out under homogeneous conditions are reproducible; the stereochemistry of reduction and the stereochemical model are based on an adequate number of known examples, none of which prove an exception to the rule; moreover, the stereoselectivities are satisfactory.

2.2.2. Cervinka's Method

Complexes of lithium aluminum hydride with alcohols or carbinol-amines (alkaloids) have been utilized for the asymmetric reduction of ketones, imines and enamines. Representative results are listed in Table 4 for the reduction of ketones with complexes of alkaloids[6].

[1] L. Horner and H. Siegel, Phosphorus 1, 199, 209 (1971).

[2] S.R. Landor, B.J. Miller, and A.R. Tatchell, Proc. Chem. Soc. 1964, 227; J. Chem. Soc. 1966, 1822; R.J.D. Evans, S.R. Landor, and J.P. Regan, Chem. Commun. 1965, 397; S.R. Landor, B.J. Miller, J.P. Regan, and A.R. Tatchell, Chem. Commun. 1966, 585.

[3] S.R. Landor and A.R. Tatchell, J. Chem. Soc. [C] 1966, 2280.

[4] H. Felkin, Bull. Soc. Chim. France 1951, 347.

[5] S.R. Landor, B.J. Miller, and A.R. Tatchell, J. Chem. Soc. [C] 1967, 197.

[6] O. Cervinka, Collect. Czech. Chem. Commun. 30, 1684 (1965); O. Cervinka, V. Suchan, and B. Maser, Collect. Czech. Chem. Commun. 30, 1693 (1965); O. Cervinka, Collect. Czech. Chem. Commun. 30, 2403 (1965).

Table 4: Enantiomeric excess and configuration of alcohols produced by asymmetric reduction of ketones with alkaloid-LiAlH$_4$ complexes[6]

$$R-\underset{\underset{O}{\|}}{C}-R' + LiAlH_3(OR^*) \longrightarrow R-\underset{\underset{OH}{|}}{CH}-R' + R^*-OH$$

$$\textbf{14} \qquad\qquad\qquad\qquad\qquad\qquad\qquad\qquad \textbf{15}$$

14	Chiral inducing agent R*OH (15)							
	(−)-quinine		(−)-cinchonidine		(+)-quinidine		(+)-cinchonine	
	e.e.(%)	conf.	e.e.(%)	conf.	e.e.(%)	conf.	e.e.(%)	conf.
H$_3$C−CO−CH(CH$_3$)$_2$	6	S						
H$_3$C−CO−C(CH$_3$)$_3$	11	S	8	S			2	R
H$_3$C−CO−C$_6$H$_{13}$	6	S	6	S			7	R
H$_3$C−CO−(aryl)−CH$_3$ (2,6-dimethylphenyl)	41	R			3	S	1	S
H$_3$C−CO−C$_6$H$_5$	48	R			23	S	18	S
H$_5$C$_6$−CO−(aryl)−CH$_3$ (2,6-dimethylphenyl)	39	S			13	R	24	R

From these results it can be seen that reduction of alkyl methyl ketones or of diaryl ketones with the complexes obtained from LiAlH$_4$ and either (−)-quinine or (−)-cinchonidine (which have the same absolute configuration at the carbon atom bearing the hydroxy and amino groups) affords the S-carbinol. Reduction of alkyl aryl ketones with the same reagent, however, gives the carbinol with the R configuration. Use of (+)-quinidine and (+)-cinchonine (which have opposite configurations to the used alkaloids) leads to reversal of carbinol configuration in the reduction (see Table 5).

It should be noted that the results obtained in these asymmetric reductions are significantly influenced by the nature of the solvent used in the reaction. The results summarized in Table 5, for example, are valid in ether but not in THF; with the latter solvent stereochemical inversion of reduction is observed. Similar inversions have also been noted in certain cases to occur as a function of temperature.

The results of the reductions cannot always be rationalized in terms of steric interactions; electronic factors must also play an important role. This follows from the fact that alkyl methyl ketones and aryl methyl ketones give products of opposite configuration, even though reductions are carried out with the same reagent under identical conditions. The empirical model proposed by Cervinka (Table 5) often constitutes only one element of the determination of the absolute configuration of secondary alcohols, and this element need not necessarily be the decisive factor.

Reduction of alkyl phenyl ketimines (22) by the complex hydride prepared from LiAlH$_4$ and (−)-menthol leads to predominant formation of the amine with the R configuration; use of (+)-borneol, on the other hand, gives preferentially the amine with the S configuration (Table 6)[7]. These reagents (LiAlH$_4$/(−)-menthol or (+)-borneol) are homogeneous, and no problems are encountered with contamination of the basic amine product by the neutral chiral reagent. The stereoselectivities which are observed are either low (alkyl phenyl ketimines) or unknown (aryl phenyl ketimines) when the corresponding amines have not been resolved. From the results of the first two entries in Table 6 it can reasonably be assumed that the amine obtained in the third example also has the R configuration. Unfortunately, however, there is no known example of the conversion of an aryl phenyl ketimine into an amine of known configuration, and hence no reliable assignment of configuration can be made with respect to the amines formed in examples 4, 5 and 6.

Table 5: Steric course of asymmetric reduction of ketones in presence of different amino-alcohols in ether (ratio $LiAlH_4$: amino-alcohol: ketone $1:1:1$)[6].

Configuration of used amino-alcohols:

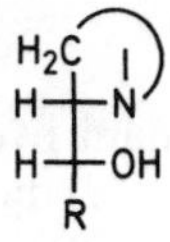

| 16,17 | 18,19 | 20,21 |

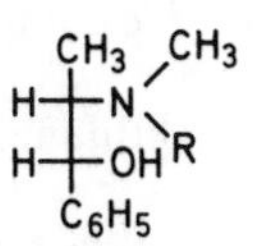

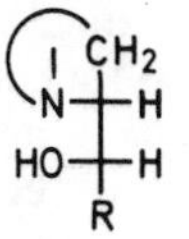

amino-alcohol	absolute configuration of the alcohol produced from the corresponding ketone			
16,17,18,19	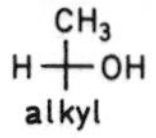 CH₃ H—OH alkyl S	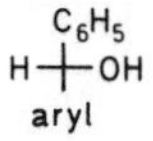 C₆H₅ H—OH aryl S	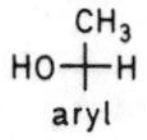 CH₃ HO—H aryl R	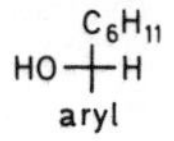 C₆H₁₁ HO—H aryl R
20,21	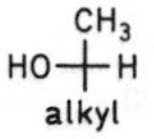 CH₃ HO—H alkyl R	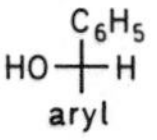 C₆H₅ HO—H aryl R	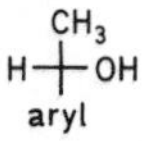 CH₃ H—OH aryl S	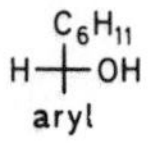 C₆H₁₁ H—OH aryl S

16: R = 6-methoxyquinol-4-yl residue: (−)-quinine
17: R = quinol-4-yl residue: (−)-cinchonidine
18: R = H: (−)-ephedrine
19: R = C_2H_5: (−)-N-ethyl-ephedrine
20: R = 6-methoxyquinol-4-yl: (+)-quinidine
21: R = quinol-4-yl: (+)-cinchonine

Table 6: Asymmetric reduction of imines by $LiAlH_4$-alcohol reagents[7]

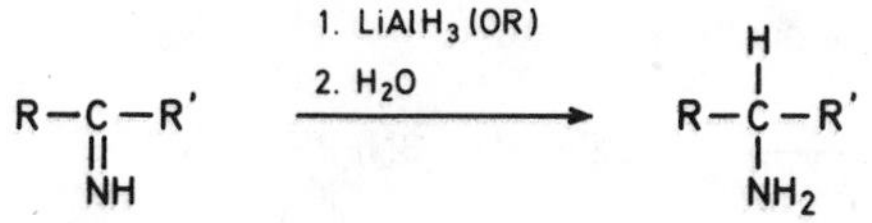

$$R—\underset{\underset{NH}{\|}}{C}—R' \xrightarrow[\text{2. } H_2O]{\text{1. } LiAlH_3 (OR)} R—\underset{\underset{NH_2}{|}}{\overset{\overset{H}{|}}{C}}—R'$$

| | **22** | | | | |
| | 22 | | 23 | | |

			Specific rotation and enantiomeric excess of **23** when ROH is					
			(−)-menthol			(+)-borneol		
Example	**22**							
	R	R'	$[a]_D^0$ (°C)	e.e. (%)	conf.	$[a]_D^0$ (°C)	e.e. (%)	conf.
1	C₆H₅	CH₃	+0.84(22)	2.2	R	−0.67(22)	1.8	S
2	C₆H₅	C₂H₅	+0.94(20)	9.9	R	−0.89(22)	9.4	S
3	C₆H₅	C₃H₇	+0.63(20)	−	−	−0.42(21)	−	−
4	C₆H₅	α-naphthyl	+4.13(18)	−	−	−1.44(18)	−	−
5	C₆H₅	O-tolyl	+4.56(22)	−	−	−	−	−
6	C₆H₅	mesityl	0.00	−	−	−	−	−
7	O-tolyl	α-naphthyl	−1.81(19)	−	−	−	−	−

The asymmetric reduction of enamines by the $LiAlH_4$/(–)-menthol complex has also been studied[8]. From the results available, however, it is evident that this method is not useful for the determination of the absolute configuration for the following reasons: owing to the insolubility of enamine salts in ether, the reactions are carried out under heterogeneous conditions; the stereoselectivities of the reactions cannot normally be determined as the products which are formed have not been resolved; finally, the results obtained vary with the composition of the reagent, especially with respect to the ratio of $LiAlH_4$ to (–)-menthol.

In conclusion, reduction by asymmetric complexes of lithium aluminum hydride can only be utilized for the determination of absolute configuration provided that standard experimental conditions are employed with series of compounds of closely related structures.

Reduction of ketones by lithium aluminum hydride in the presence of optically active alcohols or amino-alcohols
A solution of a complex hydride is prepared by addition of the optically active alcohol (11 mmol) to a solution of $LiAlH_4$ (11 mmol) in ether (1 mol). The solution is stirred for 20–30 min. and a solution of the ketone (10 mmol) in a few ml of ether is then added dropwise during 10 min. The reaction mixture is stirred for 4 hr, decomposed by water (15 ml) and 20% sulfuric acid (40 ml), and the aqueous layer extracted several times with ether. The combined extracts are dried over sodium sulfate, the solvent evaporated, and the product distilled. Products which do not contain an amino group are purified by chromatography on alumina.

Cervinka's method has recently been utilized for the determination of the absolute configuration of the alcohol 25 obtained by reduction of 1,2-ferroceno-1-cyclohexen-3-one (24) by the $LiAlH_4$/quinine complex[9]. According to Cervinka's rule, (+)-25 should have the R configuration, which confirms the configuration of 24 predicted from the Freudenberg displacement rules[10].

24   (+) – 25

2.2.3. Asymmetric Hydroboration of Olefins (Brown's Method)

Asymmetric reduction of olefins by chiral organoboranes has been extensively studied. The most widely used reagents are "di-isopinocamphenylborane" $(IPC)_2BH$ or "di-3-pinanylborane"; the latter is prepared by treatment of optically active a-pinene with diborane[11] at 0°:

The calculated quantity of a-pinene and sodium borohydride in diglyme, maintained at 0°, is treated with the theoretical amount of boron trifluoride etherate over a period of 15 min.:

$$8a\text{-pinene} + 3NaBH_4 + 4F_3B \cdot O(C_2H_5)_2 \longrightarrow 4(IPC)_2BH + 3NaBF_4 + O(C_2H_5)_2$$

The product precipitates as a thick, white solid as the reaction proceeds. The mixture is maintained for an additional 4 hr at 0°, prior to use, to ensure completion of the hydroboration reaction. The reagent appears to be quite stable under these conditions.

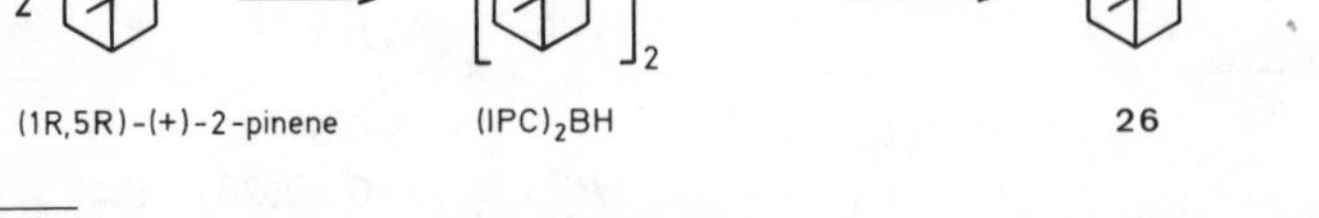

(1R,5R)-(+)-2-pinene   (IPC)$_2$BH   26

[7] O. Cervinka, V. Suchan, O. Kotynek, and V. Dudek, Collect. Czech. Chem. Commun. 30, 2484 (1965).
[8] O. Cervinka, Collect. Czech. Chem. Commun. 26, 673 (1961); 30, 2403 (1963).
[9] K. Schlögl and H. Soukup, unpublished results; cf. K. Schlögl, Top. Stereochem. 1, 39 (1967).
[10] H. Falk and K. Schlögl, Tetrahedron 22, 3047 (1966).
[11] G. Zweifel, N. Ayyangar, T. Munekuta, and H.C. Brown, J. Amer. Chem. Soc. 86, 1076 (1964).

Oxidation of (–)-(IPC)$_2$BH (prepared from (+)-a-pinene) with hydrogen peroxide gives (–)-isopinocampheol (26) the absolute configuration of which can be determined from the following considerations: hydroboration of the olefin occurs by addition of diborane to the less sterically hindered side of the molecule, i.e. opposite the bridging *gem*-dimethyl group. Thus, hydroboration is a *cis* addition reaction; finally, oxidation of the C–B bond is known to proceed with retention of configuration[12]. Results obtained in the hydroboration of olefins with (IPC)$_2$BH reveal that there is a correlation between the absolute configuration of the produced optically active alcohols and the configuration of the reagent (Table 7).

Table 7: Hydroboration of *cis*-olefins with (IPC)$_2$ BH in diglyme at 0°C

a-Pinene[a]	Olefin	Alcohol produced	conf.	e.e. (%)	Ref.
+	*cis*-2-butene	2-butanol	R	87	[11]
–	*cis*-2-butene	2-butanol	S	86	[11]
–	*cis*-2-butene[b]	2-butanol	S	78	[11]
–	*cis*-2-pentene	2-pentanol 76% 3-pentanol 24%	R	82[c]	[11]
+	*cis*-3-hexene	3-hexanol	R	91	[11]
–	*cis*-4-methyl-2-pentene	4-methyl-2-pentanol 96% 2-methyl-3-pentanol 4%	R	26[d]	[11]
+	norbornene	*exo*-norbornanol	1S, 2S	67–70	[11]
+	bicycloheptadiene	*exo*-dehydronorborneol		48–51	[13]
–	5-methylcyclopentadiene	2-methyl-3-cyclopenten-1-ol	1R, 2R	>99	[14]
+	5-methylcyclopentadiene	2-methyl-3-cyclopenten-1-ol	1S, 2S	>98	[14]

[a] both (+)-a-pinene and (–)-a-pinene were only 93–95% enantiomerically pure. The stereoselectivity (%) has to be increased by a factor of 1.05–1.08 to take this into account and to predict the e.e. (%) expected with enantiomerically pure reagent.

[b] the reaction was carried out in THF.
[c] calculated for pure 2-pentanol.
[d] calculated for pure 4-methyl-2-pentanol.

trans-Olefins and sterically hindered olefins react slowly with di-isopinocamphenylborane. Moreover, in contrast to the reactions of *cis*-olefins, which do not displace a-pinene from the reagent, *trans*-olefins eliminate about one mole of pinene per two moles of hydroborated olefin, while sterically hindered olefins eliminate about one mole of pinene per more of hydroborated olefin. Furthermore, the enantiomeric purities of the alcohols obtained from *trans* and sterically hindered alcohols after oxidation of the hydroboration adducts are low. Displacement of a-pinene from the reagent apparently indicates that hydroboration occurs not only by addition of the olefin to (IPC)$_2$BH or its dimer 27, but also by addition to its dissociation product, tri-isopinocamphenyldiborane 28 (Table 8)[15].

[12] A.G. Davies and B.P. Roberts, J. Chem. Soc. [C] 1964, 1474.
[13] K. Mislow and J.G. Berger, J. Amer. Chem. Soc. 84, 1956 (1962).
[14] J.J. Partridge, N.K. Chadha, and M.R. Uskokovic, J. Amer. Chem. Soc. 95, 532 (1973).
[15] H.C. Brown, N.R. Ayyangar, and G. Zweifel, J. Amer. Chem. Soc. 86, 1071 (1964).

Table 8: Asymmetric hydroboration of hindered olefins with 3-pinanylborane

α-Pinene[a]	Olefin	Displacement of α-pinene	Alcohol produced			Ref.
			predicted conf[11].	observed conf.	e.e. (%)	
(−) D	2-methyl-1-butene	no	R	R	21	[15]
(−) D	2,3-dimethyl-1-butene	no	R	R	30	[15]
(−) D	2-phenylpropene	no	R	R	5	[15]
(−) D	2,3,3-trimethyl-1-butene	yes	R	R[c]	−	[15]
(+) D	trans-2-butene	yes	R(−)	S(+)	13	[15]
(+) D	2-methyl-2-butene	yes	R(−)	S(+)	14	[15]
(+) T	2-methyl-2-butene	yes	R(−)	S(+)	17	[15]
(+) D	1-methylcyclopentene	yes	1R:2R	1S:2S	22	[15]
(+) T	1-methylcyclopentene	yes	1R:2R	1S:2S	17	[15]
(+) T	1-methylcyclohexene	yes	1R:2R	1S:2S	18	[15]
(+) D	3-methylcyclohexene	yes	R	S	3	[15]
(+) D	bicyclo[2.2.2]oct-2-ene	yes	2S	2R	17	[16]

[a] D = di-3-pinanylborane; T = tri-3-pinanylborane.
[b] this is the first assignment of configuration.
[c] the $[a]_D$ of (−)-2,3,3-trimethyl-1-butanol has not been determined.

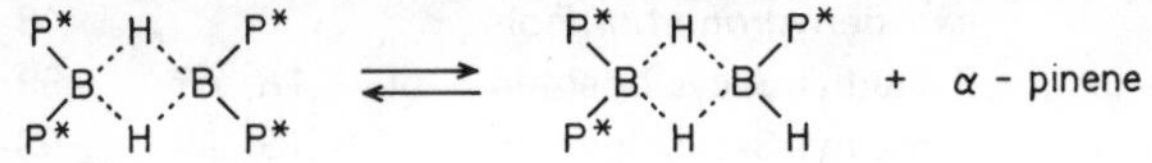

(D)   (T)
27   28

A model has been suggested[15] which may be used to rationalize and to predict the configurations of the alcohols obtained by reaction of di-3-pinanylborane with cis-olefins. Based on the steric interactions between substrate and reagent, the model involves the lower energy conformation of the organoborane reagent 29 in which the two middle planes of the α-pinene are perpendicular. There are then two possible transition states for cis-addition to an olefin, viz. 30 and 31. It has been

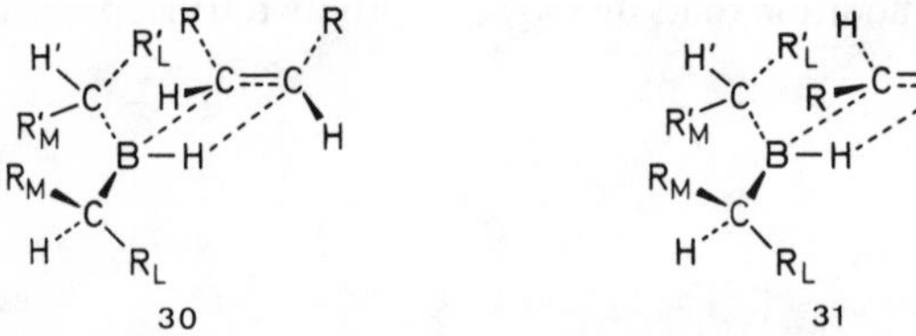

29

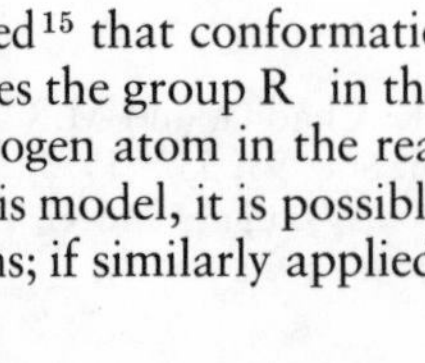

30 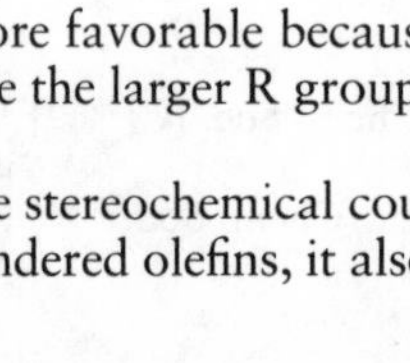   31

concluded[15] that conformation 30 is the more favorable because the hydrogen atom in the olefin then faces the group R in the reagent, while the larger R group in the olefin is more distant from the hydrogen atom in the reagent.

Using this model, it is possible to explain the stereochemical course of formation of alcohols from cis-olefins; if similarly applied to trans or hindered olefins, it also predicts formation of an alcohol of the same configuration as is obtained from a *cis*-olefin. The latter prediction is wrong, and the configurations of the alcohols which are actually obtained are always opposite to those predicted by the model. As a result of these observations, the following rule which can be applied to the asymmetric hydroboration of *trans* or sterically hindered olefins, has been formulated[11].

"Whenever displacement of *a*-pinene occurs in stoichiometric amounts in the hydroboration of olefins with (IPC)$_2$BH, the alcohol or the olefin obtained will possess the configuration opposite to that predicted on the basis of the simple addition model. For such olefins, the use of tri-isopinocamphenyldiborane will yield the same result."

Other more elaborate models have been constructed on which a better rationalization of configuration between the reagent and the product can be based[17–19]. These models are not discussed here; the Brown model, albeit imperfect, does lead to a satisfactory correlation of configuration between reagent and product. On the other hand, attention must be drawn to Mislow's results[20] which illustrate the caution which must be observed when predicting the configuration by this method. Thus, it has been found[13] that treatment of benzonorbornadiene with a mixture of (+)-*a*-pinene and diborane (1:1 molar ratio) gives, after oxidation and acetylation, either 1R, 2S-*exo*-2-benzonorbornenyl acetate or the enantiomeric 1S,2R derivative depending on the age of the reagent. These results emphasize again the importance of defining exactly the conditions under which a reaction is carried out and the nature of the reagent used, especially the manner in which it has been prepared. Only reactions which have been carried out under rigorously identical conditions and with similar types of substrates can be considered in the elaboration of a more or less empirical rule; similarly, application of the rule to other substrates will be valid only when the criteria used in the formulation of the rule are satisfied.

Reduction of ketones by (IPC)$_2$BH does not give reproducible results, while reduction of imines (Δ^1-piperideines) proceeds with poor selectivity. Consequently, these asymmetric syntheses are not useful for the determination of configuration of alcohols or imines[21].

Hydroboration of terminal olefins by (IPC)$_2$BH followed by oxidation gives alcohols of known configuration. Consequently, it is reasonable to predict the R configuration for (–)-2,3,3-trimethyl-1-butanol[11].

Di-isopinocamphenylborane has also been used in similar asymmetric syntheses for the confirmation or prediction of the absolute configuration of deuterated alcohols (Table 9).

Table 9: Asymmetric synthesis and configuration of deuterated alcohols

	32			Reagent	**33**		
R¹	R²	R³	R⁴		Deuterated alcohol	e.e. (%)	Ref.
D	H	C$_2$H$_5$	H	(DIPC)$_2$BH[a]	R(–)-1-butanol-1-d	56	[18]
D	H	C$_4$H$_9$	H	(DIPC)$_2$BH[a]	R(––-1-hexanol-1-d	42	[22]
H	D	C$_4$H$_9$	H	(DIPC)$_2$BH[a]	S(–)-1-hexanol-1-d	86	[22]
H	CH$_3$	H	CH$_3$	(DIPC)$_2$BD[b]	(2S, 3R)-2-butanol-3-d	64	[23]
H	H	H	C$_3$H$_7$	(DIPC)$_2$BD[b]	R(–)-1-pentanol-2-d	48	[24]

[a] (DIPC)$_2$BH = di-isopinocamphenylborane **27** [b] (DIPC)$_2$BD = di-isopinocamphenyldeutero-borane.

[16] H.M. Walborsky and A.E. Young, J. Org. Chem. 27, 2261 (1962).

[17] K.R. Varma and E. Caspi, Tetrahedron 24, 6365 (1968).

The absolute configuration of (−)-ethanol-1-d has been confirmed[23]. Treatment of cis-2-butene with di-3-pinanyldeuteroborane followed by oxidation of the intermediate organoborane gives $erythro$-2-butanol-3-d with the 2S,3R configuration 37 as predicted by Brown's rule. The stereochemistry and enantiomeric composition of the mixture have been determined by degradation of 37.

Cyclic imines of the type 34 have been reduced with a new reagent, lithium butyl hydrido-di(pinan-3a-yl) borate[25] (Table 10).

Table 10: Imine reduction with lithium butylhydrido-di(pinan-3-a-yl)borate prepared from (+)a-pinene

34   35   36
X = pinan-3α-yl   (predominant
R = CH₃ , C₂H₅ , C₃H₇   enantiomer)

| 34 | 36 | | |
R	e.e. (%)	conf.	yield (%)
CH₃	25	R (−)	37
C₂H₅	5	R (−)ᵃ	48
C₃H₇	4	R (−)	75

ᵃ first assignment of configuration.

[18] A. Streitwieser Jr., L.V. Verbit, and R. Bittman, J. Org. Chem. 32, 1530 (1967).

[19] D.R. Brown, S.F.A. Kettle, J. McKenna, and J.M. McKenna, Chem. Commun. 1967, 667.

[20] D.J. Sandman, K. Mislow, W.P. Giddings, J. Dirlam, and G.C. Hanson, J. Amer. Chem. Soc. 90, 4877 (1968).

[21] J.D. Morrison and H.S. Mosher, Asymmetric Organic Reactions, p. 215, Prentice Hall Int., Englewood Cliffs, 1971.

[22] H. Weber, P. Loew, and D. Arigoni, Chimia 19, 595 (1965).

[23] H. Weber, J. Seibl, and D. Arigoni, Helv. Chim. Acta 49, 741 (1966).

[24] A. Streitwieser Jr., I. Schwager, L. Verbit, and H. Rabitz, J. Org. Chem. 32, 1532 (1967).

[25] J.F. Archer, D.R. Boyd, W.R. Jackson, M.F. Grundon, and W.A. Khan, J. Chem. Soc. [C] 1971, 2560.

The absolute configurations of both (–)-2-methyl- and (–)-2-propylpiperidine were already known[26], and by analogy the *R* configuration has been assigned to (–)-2-ethylpiperidine. Application of the Brown model to this reaction indicates that **39** is the preferred transition state.

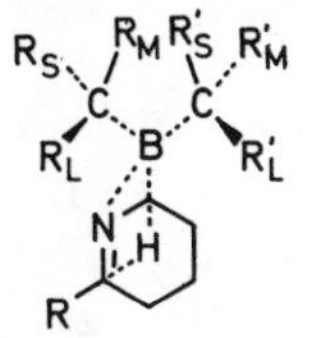

39

2.3. Asymmetric Reduction with Metal Alcoholates or Grignard Reagents

2.3.1. Asymmetric Reduction of Ketones by Chiral Grignard Reagents (Mosher's Method)

The asymmetric reduction of ketones by chiral Grignard reagents has been developed to a considerable extent. Results obtained from (+)-1-chloro-2-methylbutane and (+)-1-Chloro-2-phenylalkanes are summarized in Table 11. The stereoselectivities are not very high and the variations in

Table 11: Asymmetric reduction of ketones with chiral Grignard reagents

40 41 preferred transition state 42 predominant enantiomer

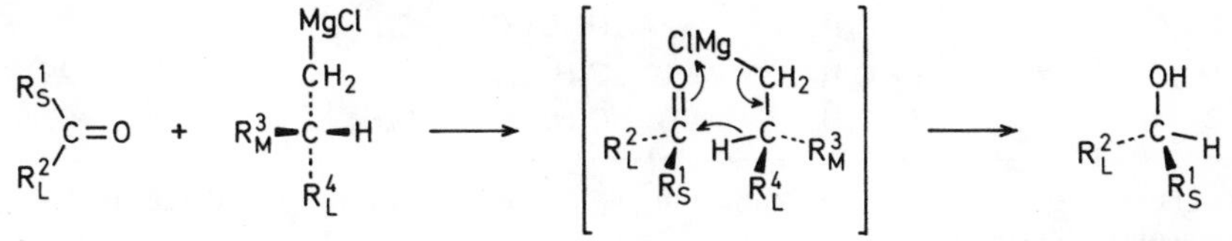

	40		41		42		
Example	R^1	R^2	R^3_M	R^4_L	conf.	e.e. (%)	Ref.
1	D	$(H_3C)_3C$	CH_3	C_2H_5	*S*(+)	12	27
2	D	C_6H_5	CH_3	C_2H_5	*S*(+)	19	28
3	CH_3	$(H_3C)_3C$	CH_3	C_2H_5	*S*(+)	13	29
4	CH_3	cyclo[c]	CH_3	C_2H_5	*S*(+)	4	30
5	CH_3	C_6H_5	CH_3	C_2H_5	*S*(–)	4	31
6	C_2H_5	$(H_3C)_3C$	CH_3	C_2H_5	*S*(–)	11	29
7	C_2H_5	cyclo	CH_3	C_2H_5	*S*(–)	9	30
8	C_2H_5	C_6H_5	CH_3	C_2H_5	*S*(–)	6	31
9	C_3H_7	$(H_3C)_3C$	CH_3	C_2H_5	*S*(–)	11	29
10	C_3H_7	cyclo	CH_3	C_2H_5	*S*(–)	9	30
11	C_3H_7	C_6H_5	CH_3	C_2H_5	*S*(–)	6	31
12	C_4H_9	$(H_3C)_3C$	CH_3	C_2H_5	*S*(–)	11	29
13	C_4H_9	cyclo	CH_3	C_2H_5	*S*(–)	9	30
14	C_4H_9	C_6H_5	CH_3	C_2H_5	*S*(–)	6[a]	31
15	$(H_3C)_2CH{-}CH_2$	$(H_3C)_3C$	CH_3	C_2H_5	*S*(–)	6	29
16	$(H_3C)_2CH{-}CH_2$	cyclo	CH_3	C_2H_5	*S*(–)	16	30

Table 11: Asymmetric reduction of ketones with chiral Grignard reagents

	40		41		42		
Example	R^1	R^2	R^3_M	R^4_L	conf.	e.e. (%)	Ref.
17	$(H_3C)_2CH-CH_2$	C_6H_5	CH_3	C_2H_5	$S(-)$	10	[31]
18	$(H_3C)_2CH$	$(H_3C)_3C$	CH_3	C_2H_5		0	[29]
19	$(H_3C)_2CH$	cyclo	CH_3	C_2H_5	$S(+)$	2	[30]
20	$(H_3C)_2CH$	C_6H_5	CH_3	C_2H_5	$S(-)$	24	[31]
21	cyclo	$(H_3C)_3C$	CH_3	C_2H_5	$S(-)$	2	[30]
22	cyclo	C_6H_5	CH_3	C_2H_5	$S(-)$[b]	25	[31]
23	$(H_3C)_3C$	C_6H_5	CH_3	C_2H_5	$S(-)$	16	[31]
24	CH_3	C_6H_5	CH_3	C_6H_5	$S(-)$	38	[32]
25	C_2H_5	C_6H_5	CH_3	C_6H_5	$S(-)$	38	[32]
26	$(H_3C)_2CH$	C_6H_5	CH_3	C_6H_5	$S(-)$	59	[32]
27	$(H_3C)_3C$	C_6H_5	CH_3	C_6H_5	$R(+)$	22	[32]
28	CH_3	C_6H_5	C_2H_5	C_6H_5	$S(-)$	47	[33]
29	C_2H_5	C_6H_5	C_2H_5	C_6H_5	$S(-)$	52	[33]
30	$(H_3C)_2CH-CH_2$	C_6H_5	C_2H_5	C_6H_5	$S(-)$	53	[33]
31	$(H_3C)_2CH$	C_6H_5	C_2H_5	C_6H_5	$S(-)$	82	[33]
32	$(H_3C)_3C$	C_6H_5	C_2H_5	C_6H_5	$S(-)$	16	[33]
33	C_2H_5	C_6H_5	$(H_3C)_2CH$	C_6H_5	$S(-)$	66	[34]
34	$(H_3C)_2CH$	C_6H_5	$(H_3C)_2CH$	C_6H_5	$S(-)$	80	[34]
35	$(H_3C)_3C$	C_6H_5	$(H_3C)_2CH$	C_6H_5	$S(-)$	91	[34]
36	D	C_6H_5	C_2H_5	C_6H_5	$R(+)$	29	[28]
37	D	C_6H_5	C_2H_5	C_6H_5	$R(+)$	67	[28]

[a] value calculated from the revised maximum rotation of 1-phenyl-1-pentanol[35].   [b] t-butyl group is considered bulkier than the cyclohexyl group.   [c] cyclo = cyclohexyl.

these values with the nature of the reactants have not always been interpreted. Nevertheless, the configuration of the alcohol which is produced can always be related to the configuration of the reagent by the following model of asymmetric induction:

Generalized model for preferred transition states in the asymmetric Grignard reduction reaction

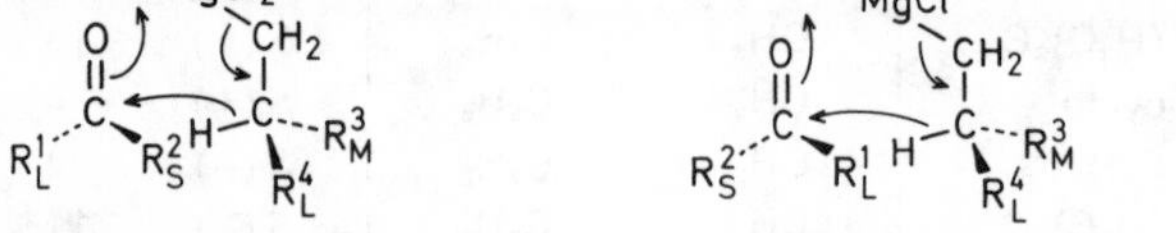

preferred transition state   non-preferred transition state

These models are based on an examination of the steric interactions occurring between the various groups in the substrate and in the reagent. It is also necessary, however, to consider electronic interactions, particularly when phenyl groups are present in both the substrate and the reagent. Under circumstances, any transition state in which the two phenyl groups are face to face must be

[26] J. Cymerman and S.K. Roy, Tetrahedron 21, 401 (1965).

[27] V.E. Althouse, E. Kaufmann, P. Löffler, K. Ueda, and H.S. Mosher, J. Amer. Chem. Soc. 83, 3138 (1961).

[28] V.E. Althouse, D.M. Feigl, W.A. Sanderson, and H.S. Mosher, J. Amer. Chem. Soc. 88, 3595 (1966).

[29] W.M. Foley, F.J. Welch, E.M. La Combe, and H.S. Mosher, J. Amer. Chem. Soc. 81, 2779 (1959).

discounted on the grounds of electronic repulsion between the two groups. In cases where a trifluoromethyl group is a constituent part of R^1 or R^2, both steric and electronic factors are involved simultaneously, and the resultant effects are difficult both to analyze and to rationalize. The influence of charge-transfer complexes on the course of asymmetric reduction of *para*-mono-substituted benzophenones has been shown[91].

Grignard reagents formed from terpene derivatives have also been utilized as reducing agents. Reductions carried out with these reagents show a certain regularity with respect to the configuration of the alcohols which are formed; the stereoselectivities are generally high. Reduction of phenyl ketones with the Grignard reagent of "pinene hydrochloride" (a mixture of bornyl- and isobornyl-magnesium chloride) gives the *R* carbinols[92]. Deuterated aldehydes have also been reduced to primary deuterated *R* alcohols by this reagent.

2.3.2. Reductions by means of Chiral Magnesium Alcoholates

Reduction of chiral compounds, especially aldehydes and ketones, with chiral magnesium alcoholates has resulted in a number of valuable determinations of configuration, and particularly of primary *a*-deuterated alcohols. The reagent is prepared by treatment of a chiral alcohol with a Grignard reagent (usually ethylmagnesium bromide):

$$R_L R_M \overset{|}{\underset{R_S}{C}} - OH \ + \ H_5C_2-MgBr \ \longrightarrow \ R_L R_M \overset{|}{\underset{R_S}{C}} - OMgBr \ + \ C_2H_6$$

(−)-Menthol, (−)-isoborneol, (+)-neomenthol and (−)-2-octanol are among the more commonly used alcohols.

(−)-Isoborneol is conveniently prepared by reduction of (+)-camphor with lithium aluminum hydride. The reduction product is contaminated with about 10% of (+)-borneol, but it has been shown that the magnesium salt of borneol does not function as a reducing agent under the reaction conditions employed[36], and hence it is possible to utilize the crude mixture obtained from the reduction of camphor for the preparation of magnesium isobornylate*.

Reduction of (+)-camphor by means of lithium aluminum deuteride followed by reaction of the isoborneol with a Grignard reagent gives the magnesium salt of (−)-isoborneol-2-*d*, which can be used for the transfer of deuterium to carbonyl derivatives. The exchange equilibrium:

$$\text{(structure with MgBr)} \ + \ R-\overset{\|}{\underset{O}{C}}-H \ \rightleftharpoons \ R-\overset{H}{\underset{OMgBr}{\overset{|}{C}}}-D \ + \ \text{(structure with O)}$$

can be strongly displaced to the right with aldehydes provided that an excess of the magnesium alcoholate is used.

The main application of these chiral alcoholate reagents involves preparation of primary deuterated alcohols and the determination of their configuration. The primary deuterated alcohols can be prepared in either of two complementary ways, viz. reduction of deuterated aldehydes with a hydrogen containing reagent, or reduction of an aldehyde with a deuterium containing reagent (Table 12). The configuration of the alcohol thus produced can be predicted from the following stereochemical models, which involve transfer of hydride (or deuteride) via a cyclic transition state:

preferred transition state   non-preferred transition state

* A method has been described whereby the borneol present in the reduction mixture may be removed by chromatography[43].

Table 12: Absolute configuration of primary deuterated alcohols by use of alkoxyma-
gnesium reagents

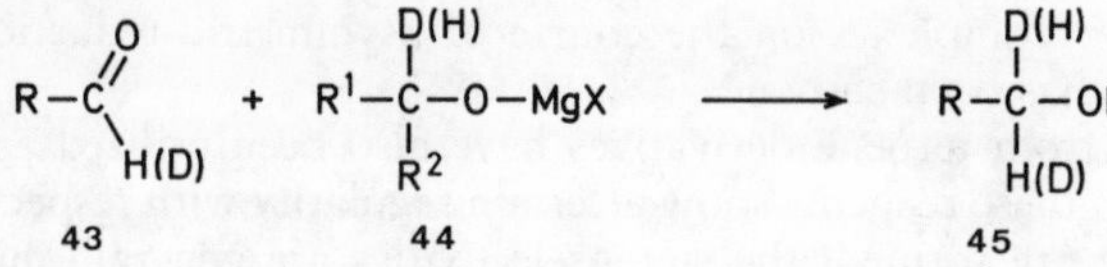

$$\underset{43}{R-\overset{\displaystyle O}{\underset{\displaystyle H(D)}{C}}} \quad + \quad \underset{44}{\overset{\displaystyle D(H)}{\underset{\displaystyle R^2}{R^1-C-O-MgX}}} \quad \longrightarrow \quad \underset{45}{\overset{\displaystyle D(H)}{\underset{\displaystyle H(D)}{R-C-OH}}}$$

Example	43	44	45		
			conf.	e.e. (%)	Ref.
1	$(H_3C)_2CH-CDO$	R (−)-2-octanol	R (−)	10	[37]
2	$(H_3C)_2CH-CHO$	S (+)-2-octanol-2-d	R (−)	8–15	[38]
3	$(H_3C)_2CH-CHO$	R (−)-2-octanol-2-d	S (+)	6	[38]
4	$(H_3C)_2CH-CHO$	(−)-isoborneol-2-d	S (+)	19	[39]
5	H_3C-CHO	‖	S (−)	44	[40]
6	H_5C_6-CDO	(−)-isoborneol	R (−)	45	[39]
7	H_5C_6-CDO	‖	R (−)	41	[41]
8	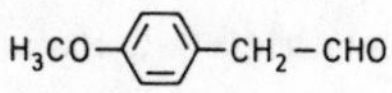 $H_3CO-\langle\ \rangle-CH_2-CHO$	(−)-isoborneol-2-d	S (−)		[42]
9	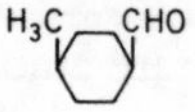 (H₃C / CHO cyclohexane structure)	‖	S (+)		[43]
10	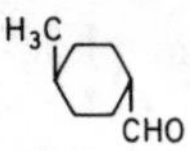 (H₃C / CHO cyclohexane structure)	‖	S (+)		[43]

The transition state of minimum energy will be that in which the 1,3-interactions between non-
bonded atoms are the less severe. The main interactions that must therefore be considered are
those between the substituent groups at the asymmetric carbon atom and the substituent groups in
the aldehyde or ketone.

Exchange of the roles of the hydrogen and deuterium between the substrate and the reagent results
necessarily in ethanol 49 which is formed predominantly and has the S configuration; 49 is then con-

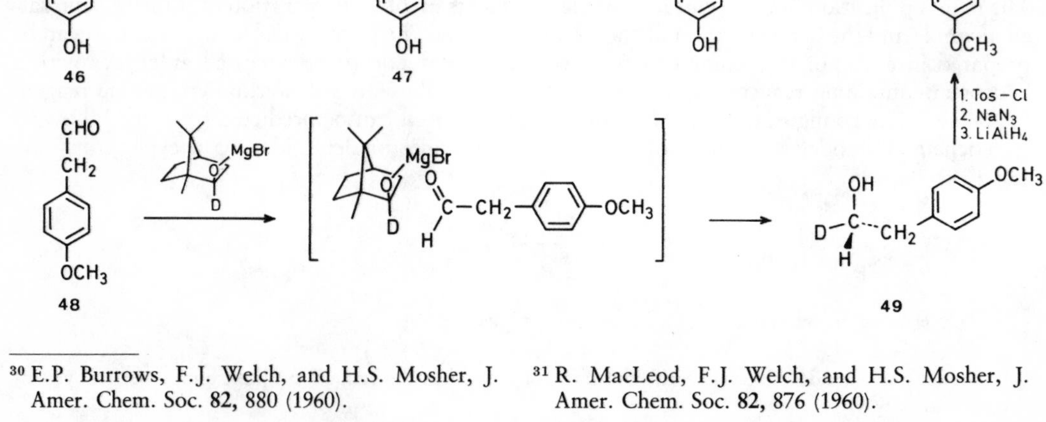

[30] E.P. Burrows, F.J. Welch, and H.S. Mosher, J. Amer. Chem. Soc. 82, 880 (1960).   [31] R. MacLeod, F.J. Welch, and H.S. Mosher, J. Amer. Chem. Soc. 82, 876 (1960).

verted via the tosylate and the azide (this step, of course, proceeds with inversion of configuration) into a-D-tyramine, which has been found to be identical with the amine obtained by enzymatic decarboxylation of tyrosine. Consequently, it follows that the decarboxylation of tyrosine by amine oxidase in D_2O proceeds with retention of configuration. The reaction is, however, an equilibrium process and it is frequently difficult to operate under reproducible conditions; hence, the variety of enantiomeric purities which has been obtained in similar or closely related reactions is not too suprising (Table 12, entries 2 and 3).

One of the applications of this asymmetric synthesis involves determination of the configuration of 2-[(−)-p-methoxyphenyl]ethanol-1-d, a compound which has been used to elucidate the steric course of the enzymatic decarboxylation of amino acids[42]. It is known that enzymatic decarboxylation of tyrosine 46 in D_2O gives tyramine-a-d (47). In order to establish the configuration of the latter compound, the reduction of p-methoxyphenylacetaldehyde (48) by the magnesium salt of (−)-isoborneol-2-d has been utilized.

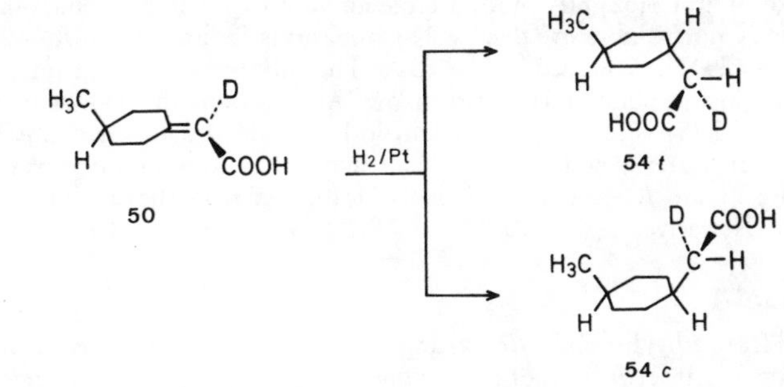

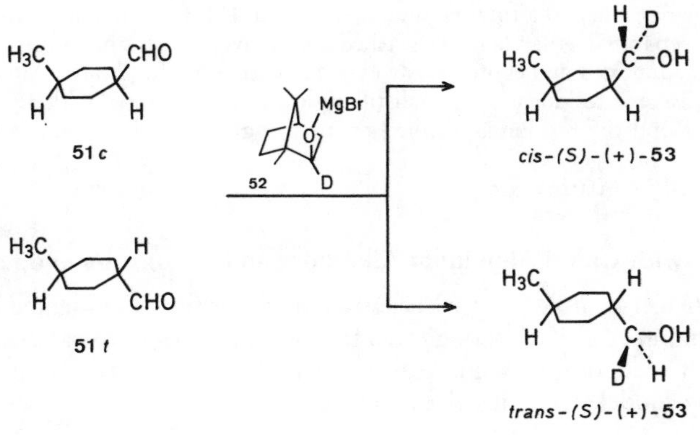

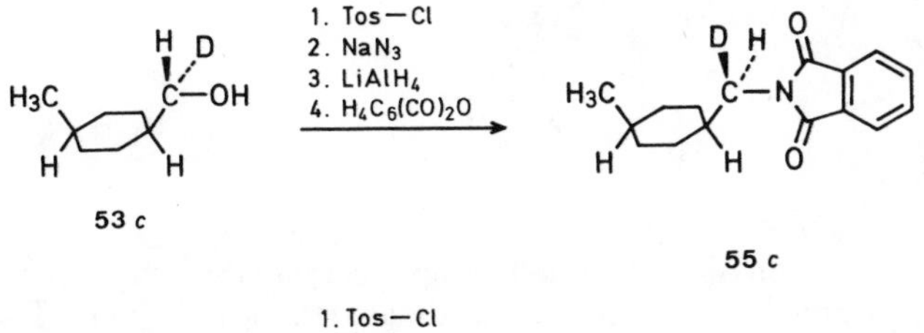

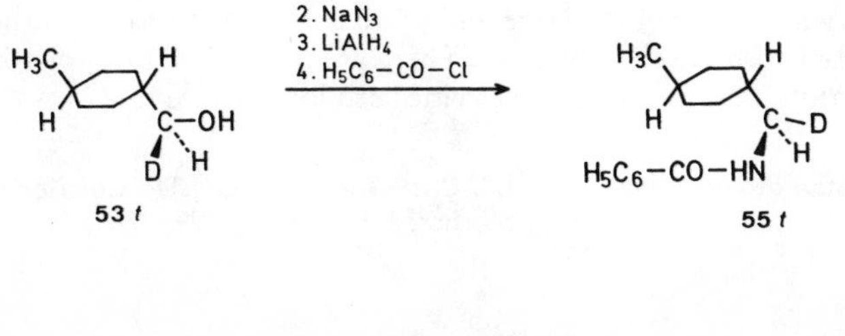

54 t

54 c

51 c

52

cis-(S)-(+)-53

51 t

trans-(S)-(+)-53

53 c

1. Tos−Cl
2. NaN₃
3. LiAlH₄
4. H₄C₆(CO)₂O

55 c

53 t

1. Tos−Cl
2. NaN₃
3. LiAlH₄
4. H₅C₆−CO−Cl

55 t

The bromomagnesium salt of (–)-isoborneol-2-d has been used in order to elucidate the stereoche-mistry of the reduction of S-(+)-4-methylcyclohexylideneacetic acid (50), which is axially disym-metric[43]. According to the stereochemical model, reduction of cis- and trans-4-methylcyclohex-ylacetaldehyde (51c and 51t), by means of 52 gives the primary deuterated alcohols 53c and 53t respectively, both with the S configuration. Catalytic hydrogenation of 50 leads to a 2:1 mixture of the trans-(+)-54t and cis-(–)-54c compounds via the intermediacy of compounds 55c and 55t. The configuration of the products can be determined by correlation with 53c and 53t. In this way, 54t has been assigned the S and 54c the R configuration. These results confirm the hypothesis that catalytic reduction of 50 proceeds via cis-addition of hydrogen to the double bond.

Asymmetric synthesis of benzyl-a-d-alcohol[41]

To a solution of propylmagnesium bromide prepared from propyl bromide and magnesium (9.7 g, 0.4 mol) in dry ether, maintained at 0°, is added slowly a dry ethereal solution of a mixture of isoborneol and borneol (prepared by reduction of natural gum camphor with LiAlH$_4$) until the evolution of the gas has ceases. At the end of the addition of the alcohol mixture (62 g, 0.4 mol), a large amount of white precipitate has formed. Isobornyloxymagnesium bromide is not soluble in ether[36]. The apparatus is fitted for distillation with a Vigreux column, and dry benzene (700 ml) is added to the flask. The mixture is distilled until the vapor temperature reaches 75°, at which time the solution is homogeneous. After cooling to room temperature, the flask is again arranged for stirring and 25 g (0.23 mol) benzaldehyde-1-d is added with stirring. After stirring for 3 hr at room temperature, enough water is added to stop the reaction and to obtain two phases, a clear organic phase and a thick white precipitate. R(–)-Benzyl-a-d-alcohol is isolated from the organic phase in 59 % yield in the form of the phthalate derivative.

Asymmetric synthesis of butanol-1-d[44]

To the Grignard reagent prepared from ethyl bromide (67.5 g) and magnesium (15.1 g) is added with stirring 2-octanol-2-d (81.5 g, 0.62 mol) (prepared by reduction of 2-octanone with LiAlH$_4$ and subsequent resolution) having $[a]_D^{20} = 7.62°$ (neat). To this mixture, stirred in an ice-bath, is then added freshly distilled butyralde-hyde (44.6 g, 0.62 mol) followed by dry ether to a total volume of 1 l. After 4 hr at room temperature, dilute hydrochloric acid is added. The separated ether layer is washed successively with anhydrous potassium carbonate. The aqueous layers are combined and continuously extrated with ether for 2 days. After washing and drying, removal of the solvent leaves a residue which, on distillation, affords a material with b.p. 95–115°. Ether is removed from the extract and the residue is distilled through a glass-spiral fractionating column collecting 21.7 ml
b.p.: 114–116° (total yield 43 %) $[a]_D^{25} = -0.026°$.

2.3.3. Asymmetric Reductions with Chiral Aluminum Alkoxides and Alkoxyaluminodichlorides

The asymmetric version of the Meerwein-Ponndorf-Verley reaction was first investigated by Doer-ing and Young[45] and by Jackmann et al.[46]. Although this reaction involves both catalysis and an equilibrium, the steric course of reduction may, in cases where an optically active alcohol results, be interpreted by the following model which involves a cyclic transition state:

X = OR , Cl

This means that the electrophilic carbon of the carbonyl group is close to the hydrogen atom in the aluminum complex, while the carbonyl oxygen atom is coordinated to the aluminum. The favored transition state is then that in which each of the large and small substituent groups in the reagent faces respectively the groups R_S and R_L in the substrate. There are only a few examples known of this type of asymmetric reduction, and the stereoselectivities are low (Table 13).

[32] C. Aaron unpublished results, Stanford University, 1964.

[33] J.S. Birtwistle, K. Lee, J.D. Morrison, and H.S. Mosher, J. Org. Chem. 29, 37 (1964).

Table 13: Reduction of ketones with chiral aluminum alkoxides

R'	R	**56**		
		conf.	e. e. (%)	Ref.
$CH(CH_3)_2$	$c\text{-}C_6H_{11}$	$S(+)$	22	[45]
C_2H_5	$i\text{-}C_6H_{13}$	$S(+)$	6	[45]
$C(CH_3)_3$	$n\text{-}C_6H_{13}$	$S(+)$	6	[46]

Reduction of ketones with alkoxyaluminodichlorides takes place with significant asymmetric induction. These reagents, which have never been isolated, are prepared by reaction of a chiral alcohol (4 mol) with lithium aluminum hydride (1 mol) and aluminum chloride (3 mol):

$$LiAlH_4 \;+ 4ROH \longrightarrow LiAl(OR)_4 + 4H_2$$
$$LiAl(OR)_4 + 3AlCl_3 \longrightarrow LiCl \quad + 4AlCl_2OR$$

Many ketones have been reduced with (−)-isobornyloxyaluminum dichloride, formed by treatment of isoborneol with $HAlCl_2$ (Table 14). Reduction proceeds via hydride transfer, and the isomer which is formed preferentially always has the stereoformula 57, in agreement with the transition state of lower energy. This asymmetric synthesis has not yet been used for the determination of the

Table 14: Reduction of ketones with (−)-isobornyloxyaluminum dichloride

Ketone	Carbinol produced[a]		
	e. e. (%)	yield (%)	Ref.
$H_5C_2-CO-CH_3$	3	20–25	[47]
$(H_3C)_2CH-CH_2-CO-CH_3$	5	30–33	[47]
$(H_3C)_2CH-CO-CH_3$	15	20–28	[47]
$(H_3C)_3C-CO-CH_3$	18	12–15	[47, 48]
$H_5C_6-CO-CH_3$	27	50	[49]
$H_5C_6-CO-C_2H_5$	38		[49]
$H_5C_6-CO-C_3H_7$	44		[49]
$H_5C_6-CO-CH_2-CH(CH_3)_2$	66		[49]
$H_5C_6-CO-CH(CH_3)_2$	84		[49]
$H_5C_6-CO-C_6H_{11}-c$	40		[49]
$H_5C_6-CO-C(CH_3)_3$	23		[49]

[a] all carbinols exhibit R configuration.

absolute configuration of alcohols. Experimentally, the order in which the various operations are carried out is of some importance. Thus, while in the preparation of the reagent the order of addition of the chiral alcohol or the $HAlCl_2$ is of little significance, in the reduction step, it is important that the ketone is added last.

To an ice-cold stirred solution of anhydrous aluminum chloride (5.34 g, 0.04 mol) in ether (50 ml) is added a $1M$ ethereal solution of $LiAlH_4$ (10 ml, 0.01 mol) all at once[47]. After 30 min. (–)-isoborneol (6.2 g, 0.04 mol) (or an equivalent mixture of isoborneol and borneol obtained from camphor) in ether (30 ml) is slowly added. A slight excess of (–)-isoborneol is generally taken in order to ensure that all the hydride reacts. The reaction vessel is then removed from the ice-bath and the mixture stirred for a few minutes more. A solution of the ketone (0.03 mol) in ether (20 ml) is then slowly introduced into the cold solution of the reagent within 15 min. during which time the mixture warms up to room temperature. Stirring is continued for 30 min. more at this temperature to complete the reduction, and the solution then cooled and decomposed by careful addition of $3N$ H_2SO_4. The ethereal layer is separated the aqueous solution extracted twice with alcohol-free ether, the combined extracts once washed with a little water and dried over anhydrous K_2CO_3 overnight. The ether is distilled off, and isolation of the carbinols is carried out according to their boiling points. Distillation is used for lower boiling alcohols, and steam distillation for higher boiling ones.

3.　Determination of Absolute Configuration by means of Kinetic Resolution

Determination of configuration has frequently been effected on the basis of kinetic resolution. When the absolute configuration of the reagent used is known, the configuration of the substrate which is obtained in excess can be deduced by consideration of the stereochemical course of the reaction.

3.1.　Configuration of Biphenyls: Mislow's Method

The reduction of *racemic* 1,11-dinitro-5 *H*-6,7-dihydrodibenzo[*a, c*]cyclohepten-6-one 58 by *S*(+)-methyl-*t*-butylcarbinol in the presence of aluminum *t*-butoxide[50] has been utilized as a means of determining the configuration of the biphenyl ketone. Examination of the diastereoisomeric transition states for reduction shows that 59 A is preferred, i.e., 58 A will be reduced more rapidly than 58 B, which will thus constitute the major portion of any unreduced ketone. The dextrorotatory

[34] J.L. Schmiegel, Ph. D. Thesis, Stanford University, 1967; Diss. Abstr. 28, 4507 (1967).

[35] A. Horeau, J.P. Guetté, and R. Weidmann, Bull. Soc. Chim. France 1966, 3513.

[36] G. Vavon and A. Antonini, C.R. Acad. Sci., Paris 232, 1120 (1951).

[37] A. Streitwieser, Jr., and W.D. Schäffer, J. Amer. Chem. Soc. 78, 5597 (1956).

[38] A Streitwieser, Jr., J. Amer. Chem. Soc. 75, 5014 (1953).

[39] A. Streitwieser Jr., J.R. Wolfe, and W.D. Schäffer, Tetrahedron 6, 338 (1959).

[40] A. Streitwieser and M.R. Granger, J. Org. Chem. 32, 1528 (1967).

[41] A. Streitwieser Jr. and J.R. Wolfe, J. Amer. Chem. Soc. 79, 903 (1957).

[42] B. Belleau and J. Burba, J. Amer. Chem. Soc. 82, 5751 (1960).

[43] H. Gerlach, Helv. Chim. Acta 49, 1291 (1966).

[44] A. Streitwieser Jr., J. Amer. Chem. Soc. 77, 1117 (1955).

[45] W. von E. Döring and R.W. Young, J. Amer. Chem. Soc. 72, 631 (1950).

[46] L.M. Jackman, J.A. Mills, and J.S. Shannon, J. Amer. Chem. Soc. 72, 4184 (1950).

[47] D. Nasipuri and G. Sarkar, J. Indian Chem. Soc. 44, 425 (1967); D. Nasipuri and G. Sarkar, J. Indian Chem. Soc. 44, 556 (1967).

[48] D. Mea-Jacheet and A. Horeau, Bull. Soc. Chim. France 1966, 3040.

[49] D. Nasipuri and G. Sarkar, J. Indian Chem. Soc. 44, 165 (1967).

[50] P. Newman, P. Rutkin, and K. Mislow, J. Amer. Chem. Soc. 80, 465 (1958); K. Mislow and F.A. McGinn, 80, 6036 (1958); K. Mislow, R.E. O'Brien, and H. Schäffer, 84, 1940 (1962); K. Mislow, R. Graeve, A.J. Gordon, and G.H. Wahi, 86, 1733 (1964).

ketone is thus assigned the *S* configuration; the configurations of the alcohols **60** have been assigned in a similar manner.

(−)-*R*-**58A**   **59A**   **60**

(+)-*S*-**58B**   **59B**   **60**

3.2.   Configuration of Carboxylic Acid Chlorides: Bestmann's Method

A novel procedure has been introduced for the determination of the absolute configuration of carboxylic acids based on the kinetic resolution of benzylidene-methyl-phenyl-propylphosphorane (**61**) by the optically active acid chloride **62**[51]. Reaction of **62** with **61** gives the acylated phosphonium salt **63** which reacts further with **61** in a transylidation reaction to give the acyl ylide and the phosphonium salt **64**, which precipitates from solution. The reactions of both **62** and **63** with

61, however, occur preferentially with one of the enantiomers of the latter compound. Hence, an excess of the other enantiomer of **61** accumulates in solution, while, conversely, an excess of the diastereoisomeric ylide of opposite configuration is produced as a result of the overall reaction sequence[52–54].

It has been shown that the absolute configuration of the phosphonium salt **64** (the enantiomer formed predominantly) is related to the absolute configuration of the acid chloride used; this correlation has been established by application of the Ugi-Ruch rule[55, 56]. Thus, a Newmann

[51] H. J. Bestmann, H. Scholz, and E. Kranz, Angew. Chem. Int. Ed. **9**, 796 (1970).

[52] H. J. Bestmann and I. Tömösközi, Tetrahedron **24**, 3299 (1968).

[53] H. J. Bestmann, Chem. Ber. **95**, 58 (1962); H. J. Bestmann and B. Arnason, Chem. Ber. **95**, 1513 (1962).

[54] H. J. Bestmann, Angew. Chem. Int. Ed. **4**, 583 (1965).

[55] E. Ruch and I. Ugi, Theor. Chim. Acta **4**, 287 (1966).

[56] E. Ruch and I. Ugi, Top. Stereochem. **4**, 99 (1969).

[56] I. Ugi, Z. Naturforsch. **20b**, 405 (1965).

projection of the acid chloride is used, in which the chlorine atom is set to the rear of the asymmetric carbon atom, to the substituent groups of which are assigned the symbols λ_1, λ_2 and λ_3 in a clockwise manner as shown in 65. The sign of the asymmetric induction is then given by the sign of

65

the chirality product $\chi = (\lambda_1 - \lambda_2)(\lambda_2 - \lambda_3)(\lambda_3 - \lambda_1)$. If the configuration of the acid chloride is correctly assigned in 65 then the sign of the chirality product will be the same as the sign of the isolated product 64.

Thus, for the determination of the absolute configuration of an acid, its Newman projection is drawn with the three substituents at the asymmetric carbon atom arranged in any order, and to each is assigned a λ, the numbering being in a clockwise fashion. Appropriate λ values are then assigned using either the tables provided by Ugi[56] or basing the assignment merely on the relative size of the substituents (the larger the substituent, the higher the value). If the sign of the rotatory power of the isolated salt 64 is the same as that of the previously defined chirality product, then the configuration of the acid has been correctly drawn; if the signs are different then the acid has the opposite configuration to that drawn. Excellent agreement has been found between predicted and known configuration using this method, and representative results are summarized in Table 15. It should be noted that, in order to draw conclusions regarding the absolute configuration of a particular acid chloride, it is necessary when using this method to isolate a phosphonium chloride of reasonable optical purity (1 or 2%).

Table 15: Determination of the absolute configurations of acid chlorides[51]

Example	Acid chloride	Sign of opt. rot. of 64 (589 nm, CH$_3$OH)	Sign of chirality parameter of 62	Absolute configuration	
				found	litt.
1	(+)-hydratropoyl	−	−	S	S
2	(−)-2-phenylbutyryl	+	+	R	R
3	(+)-2-phenylbutyryl	−	−	S	S
4	(−)-N-phthaloylvalyl	+	+	S	S
5	(−)-N-phthaloylphenylalanyl	+	+	S	S
6	(+)-O-methylmandeloyl	−	−	S	S
7	(−)-O-methylmandeloyl	+	+	R	R
8	(−)-N-phthaloylalanyl	+	+	S	S
9	(−)-O-methyllactoyl	−	−	S	S
10	(−)-O-methyllactoyl	+	+	R	R
11	(−)-O-benzoyllactoyl	+	+	R	R
12	(−)-N-phthaloylleucyl	+	+	S	S
13	(−)-2-chloro-4-methylvaleryl	+	+	S	S
14	(+)-2-chloropropionyl	+	+	S	S
15	(+)-2-chloro-3-methylbutyryl	+	+	S	S
16	(−)-menthyloxyformyl	+	+	3R	3R
17	(−)-3-acetoxy-5-etiocholenoyl	+	+	17R	

A filtered solution of the ylide **61** in tetrahydrofuran is prepared by treatment of benzyl-methyl-phenyl-propyl-phosphonium bromide (6.76 g, 20 mmol) with sodium amide (from 0.5 g of sodium) under dry nitrogen[58]. To the stirred solution is added dropwise at room temperature a solution of the optically active acid chloride **62** (10 mmol) in tetrahydrofuran to precipitate **64**. The phosphonium salt **64** is collected by filtration, washed with benzene, dried, and its optical rotation determined. The optical yield is 6–7%. The following values have been found for (+)-*S* – **64** with an optical purity of 86%:

$[a]_{589} = +36.2$, $[a]_{578} = +38.5$, $[a]_{546} = +44.9$, $[a]_{436} = +84.6$, $[a]_{365} = +150.7$ (c = 0.54 in methanol).

3.3   Configuration of Olefins: Brown's Method

A number of *racemic,* sterically unhindered olefins have been resolved via partial hydroboration with di-isopinocamphenylborane. The more reactive of the enantiomeric olefins can be predicted from the stereochemical model which represents the diastereoisomeric transition states for hydroboration, and hence the enantiomer which is preferentially unattacked during the resolution can be identified. Thus, in the kinetic resolution of 3-methylcyclopentene (**66**) with "di-3-pinanylborane", a residual dextrorotatory olefin of optical purity 65% has been isolated. The configuration

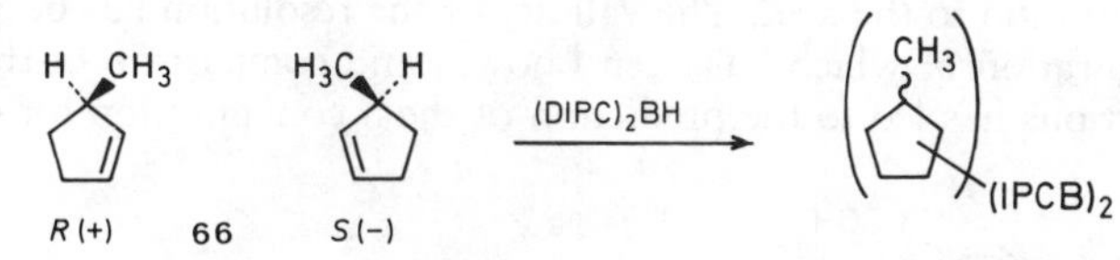

$t = 0$:   0.15 mol (*racemic* olefin), 0.12 mol $(DiPC)_2BH$
recovered olefin: 0.03 mol [82.5% *R*(+) and 17.5% *S*(–)]

predicted for this compound from an examination of the model (see p. 106) is *R*. The configurations of 3-ethylcyclopentene, 1-methylnorbornene and 4-methylcyclohexene have been elucidated in a similar manner (Table 16).

Table 16: Configuration of olefins by kinetic resolution[a]

Olefin	Absolute Configuration		Ref.
	predicted	observed	
3-methylcyclopentene	*R*	*R*	[59]
3-ethylcyclopentene	*R*	*R*	[59]
1-methylnorbornene	1*S*, 4*R*	1*S*, 4*R*	[59]
4-methylcyclohexene	*R*	*R*	[60]
1,3-dialkylallenes[b]	*R*		[61]

[a] reagent prepared from (+)-α-pinene.
[b] reagent prepared from (–)-α-pinene.

The kinetic resolution of a number of allenes has been effected by the use of pinanyldiboranes (prepared from (–)-pinene)[61, 62]. In each case the reaction mixture, after partial hydroboration of the racemic allenes, has been found to contain an excess of the enantiomeric allene with the *R*

[59] H.C. Brown, N.R. Ayyangar, and G. Zweifel, J. Amer. Chem. Soc. **86**, 397 (1964).
[60] S.I. Goldberg and F.L. Lam, J. Org. Chem. **31**, 240 (1966).
[61] W.R. Moore, H.W. Anderson, and S.D. Clark, J. Amer. Chem. Soc. **95**, 835 (1973).
[62] W.L. Waters, W.S. Linn, and M.C. Caserio, J. Amer. Chem. Soc. **90**, 6741 (1968).

configuration, irrespective of the age or nature of the reagent (tetra-, tri-, di-pinanyl-diboranes). The optical purities of the allenes thus obtained (1,3-dimethyl-, 1,3-diethyl-, 1,3-dipropyl-, and 1,3-di-t-butyl-allene) are not known, as none of these compounds has ever been completely resolved.

It has been shown that the treatment of N,N-diferrocenylcarbodiimide (67) with 6,6'-dinitrodi-phenic acid in anhydrous benzene results in kinetic resolution with formation of the corresponding acylurea; the carbodiimide which does not react with the acid has been found to be optically

active. The R configuration is assigned to 67 on the basis of stereochemical considerations on the nature of the favored transition state[63].

Kinetic resolution of (+)-2,2-paracyclophanecarboxylic acid 68 with (−)-α-phenylethylamine per-mits assignment of the S configuration to the acid. The validity of the resolution has been tested with the acid (−)-69, the configuration of which has been known, and comparison of the steric course for each of the two reactions has led to the prediction of the S configuration for 68[64].

4.   Determination of Absolute Configurations by Enzymatic Methods

Determination of the configuration of organic compounds by the use of enzymes can be accom-plished in two ways:

(a) asymmetric synthesis of a compound by means of an enzyme of known stereochemical speci-ficity;

(b) degradation of a racemic compound by means of an enzyme (enzymatic resolution). If the stereospecificity of the enzyme for the particular type of substrate is known in the latter case, prediction of configuration of the non-metabolized enantiomer is simplified.

With these methods it is necessary to have available enzymes which show a high "product specific-ity", i.e. which can react with a prochiral substrate to give a product of high optical purity or, in the case of kinetic resolution, which metabolize only one enantiomer of a racemic mixture. Ideally, it is also advantageous to have available enzymes which show a low "substrate specificity", i.e. which can be utilized with as wide a range as possible of "non-physiological" compounds.

4.1.   Enzymatic Asymmetric Synthesis

The following discussion is concerned with two selected examples of enzymatic asymmetric synthesis.

[63] K. Schlögl, and H. Mechtler, Angew. Chem. Int. Ed. 5, 596 (1966).

[64] H. Falk and K. Schlögl, Angew. Chem. Int. Ed. 7, 383 (1969).

4.1.1. Reduction by Active Fermenting Yeast

It has long been known that many "non-physiological" compounds can be reduced by yeast, and that if the material being reduced is prochiral, the product obtained is generally optically active. Using this approach it has been shown that reduction of various ketones gives carbinols which generally have the configuration depicted in the stereoformula 70[65].

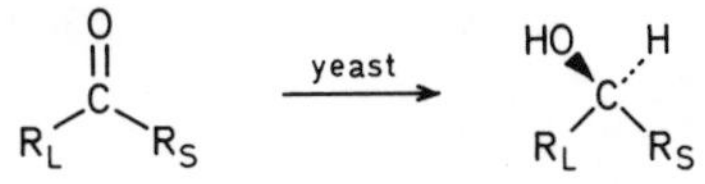

70

The stereoselectivities in these reductions vary between 60 and 90%. Deuterated aldehydes can be reduced similarly[66]:

$R = CH_3$, C_3H_7, $C(CH_3)_3$, C_6H_5

Prediction of configuration on the basis of MacLeod's results is apparently only valid, however, when the substituent groups at the carbonyl function are either hydrogen, as in the case of aldehydes, or hydrocarbon, as in the case of ketones. For example, reduction of biacetyl gives (−)-2,3-butanediol[67] (71), the configuration of which is opposite to that predicted by MacLeod's model; it is assumed that the CH_3 group is the S substituent and the $COCH_3$ group the L substituent.

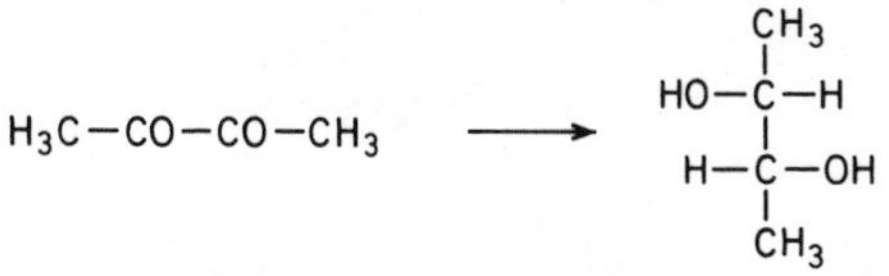

$$H_3C-CO-CO-CH_3 \longrightarrow$$

71

Some α-ketols have been reduced to enantiomerically pure α-diols[93]. β,γ- and δ-Oxo acids have also been reduced with yeast, but no exact information of the configuration of the products obtained is available.

4.1.2. Reduction by C. Falcata

About fifty compounds have been reduced by C. falcata, and in most cases the products obtained have been found to exibit S configuration. Reduction of the ketone 72 by C. falcata leads to predominant formation of the isomer 73; hence, the enzyme does exhibit a high "product stereos-

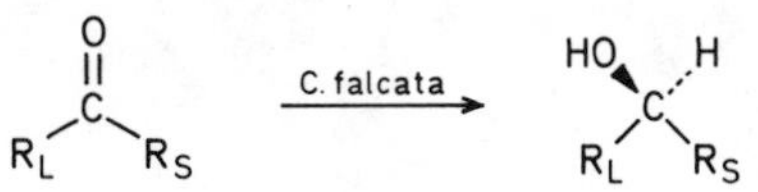

72   73

pecificity" and a low "substrate specificity" – properties which are valuable in the use of this enzyme for the determination of absolute configuration.

[65] R. MacLeod, H. Prosser, K. Fikentscher, S. Lanyi, and H.S. Mosher, Biochemistry 3, 838 (1964).
[65] V.E. Althouse, D.M. Feigl, W.A. Sargeson, and H.S. Mosher, J. Amer. Chem. Soc. 88, 4595 (1966).
[67] C. Neuberg and F.F. Nord, Ber. 52B, 2248 (1919).
[68] V. Prelog and W. Acklin, Helv. Chim. Acta 39, 748 (1956).

Table 17: Determination of configuration by the use of C. falcata.

Substrate	Products	Ref.
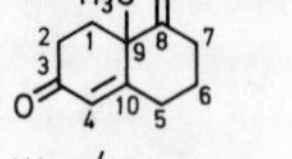 (±)-Δ⁴-9-methyl-octalin-3,8-dione	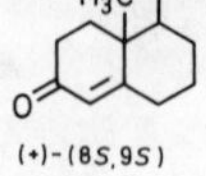 (+)-(8S,9S)	68
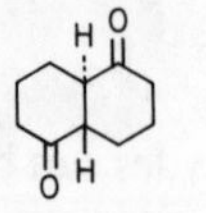 trans-decalin-1,5-dione	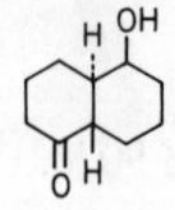 (5S,9S,10R) 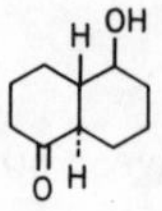 (5S,9R,10S) 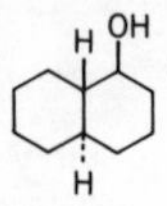 (1S,5S,9R,10S)	68
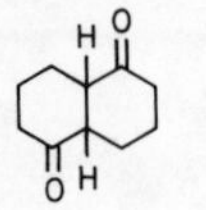 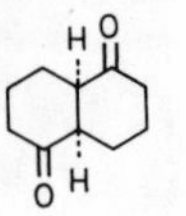 (±)cis-decalin-1,5-dione	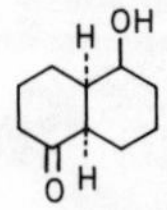 (5S,9R,10R) 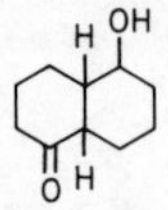 (5S,9S,10S) 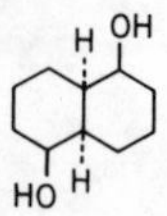 (1S,5S,9R,10R) 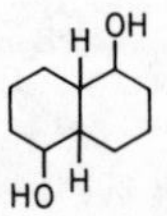 (1S,5S,9S,10S)	69
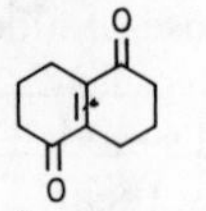 Δ⁹-octalin-1,5-dione	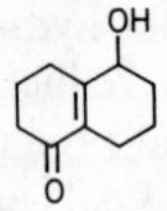 (5S)-5-hydroxy-1-octalone	70
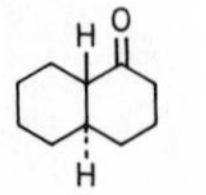 (±)-trans-decalone (9R,10S) + (9S,10R)	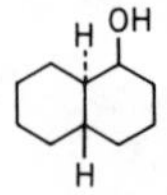 (1S,9R,10S) + (1S,9S,10R)	71
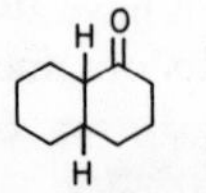 (±)-1-cis-decalone (9S,10S) + (9R,10R)	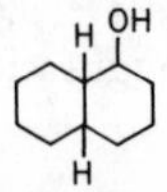 (1S,9S,10S) + (1S,9R,10R)	71
(10aR)	(10aR, 1S)	71
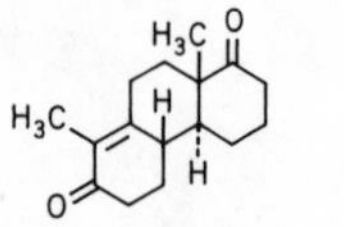 (10aS)	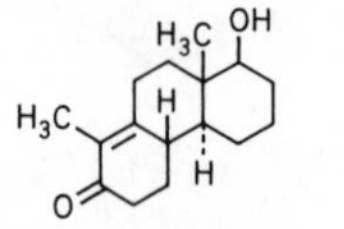 (10aS, 1S)	71
(10aR)	(10aR,1S)	71
(S)-benzoin	(S,S)-hydrobenzoin	72
(R)-benzoin	inactive hydrobenzoin	73
benzil	(S)-benzoin (56% e.e.)	73

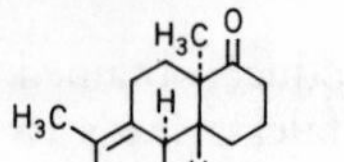

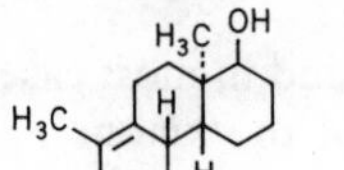

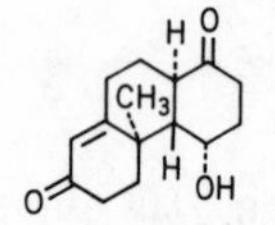

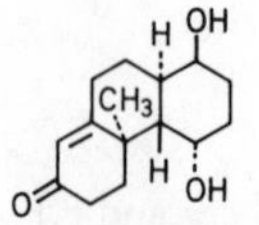

4.2. Absolute Configuration by means of Enzymatic Resolution

4.2.1. Utilization of or Degradation by Microorganisms

Implicit in the application of biological agents to the determination of configuration is the assumption that the particular microorganism, or active fraction thereof, is capable of metabolising the chemical structure of a given racemate and, further, that metabolism of one of the antipodes proceeds significantly faster than metabolism of the other.

Ehrlich[74], working with yeast as the biological resolving agent, has shown that, in the case of amino acids, it preferentially consumes the naturally occurring enantiomer in proteins, i.e. the L form. The other enantiomer is not normally affected, and can be recovered from cultures in a state of high isomeric purity. Starting with *racemic* sugars, Fischer has similarly prepared the non-naturally occurring forms of hexoses[75].

One particularly interesting application of the use of yeast is the determination of the stereochemical correlation between the β-asymmetric centers of the optical isomers of isoleucine and alloisoleucine. Treatment of the mixture of epimers, formed by racemization of the a-asymmetric center of (+)-isoleucine (**74**), with yeast results in the isolation of (–)-alloisoleucine (**75**). Consequently,

$$
\begin{array}{c}
COOH \\
H_2N-C-H \\
H_3C-C-H \\
C_2H_5 \\
\mathbf{74}
\end{array}
\xrightarrow[\nabla,\ pressure]{Ba(OH)_2}
\begin{array}{c}
COOH \\
H_2N-C-H \\
H_3C-C-H \\
C_2H_5
\end{array}
+
\begin{array}{c}
COOH \\
H-C-NH_2 \\
H_3C-C-H \\
C_2H_5
\end{array}
\xrightarrow{yeast}
\begin{array}{c}
COOH \\
H-C-NH_2 \\
H_3C-C-H \\
C_2H_5 \\
\mathbf{75}
\end{array}
$$

the absolute configuration of the β-asymmetric carbon atoms in (+)-isoleucine and (–)-alloisoleucine is the same[76]. It should be noted, however, that the antipodal specificity of microorganisms may change with variation in culture feeding[77].

4.2.2. Asymmetric Oxidation

Treatment of a *racemic* mixture of amino acid derivatives

$$
\begin{array}{c}
R-CH-COOH \\
NH-R'
\end{array}
$$

R' = H, alkyl

with oxidases results in the transformation of the active antipode into an a-oxo acid; the other antipode, which is unaffected by the oxidase, can then be isolated. For example, the D-configuration was assigned to (–)-allothreonine[78] on this basis, as this isomer is oxidized by the action of hog kidney D-amino acid oxidase, while (+)-allothreonine is unaffected. A table of the structural and antipodal specificities of several L- and D-amino acid oxidases has been established[79].

The absolute configuration of monotritiated glycine which was prepared by incubation of *dl*-glycine-1*t* with serine hydroxymethylase in tritium oxide has been defined[80].

[69] P. Baumann and V. Prelog, Helv. Chim. Acta **41**, 2739 (1958).

[70] P. Baumann and V. Prelog, Helv. Chim. Acta **42**, 736 (1959).

[71] W. Acklin, V. Prelog, F. Schenker, B. Serdarevic, and P. Walter, Helv. Chim. Acta **48**, 1725 (1965).

[72] V. Prelog, Ciba Found. Study Group **2**, 79 (1959).

[73] W. Acklin, Z. Kis, and V. Prelog, Croat. Chem. Acta **37**, 11 (1965).

[74] F. Ehrlich, Biochem. Z. **1**, 8 (1906).

[75] E. Fischer, Z. Physiol. Chem. **26**, (1898).

[76] F. Ehrlich, Biochem. Z. **63**, 397 (1914); F. Ehrlich, Ber. **40**, 2538 (1907).

[77] P. Greenstein and M. Winitz, Chemistry of the Amino Acids, p. 137, John Wiley and Sons, 1961.

[78] J.R. Klein and P. Handler, J. Biol. Chem. **139**, 103 (1941).

[79] P. Greenstein and M. Winitz, Chemistry of the Amino Acids, p. 146, John Wiley and Sons, 1961.

[80] M. Akhtar and P.M. Jordan, Tetrahedron Lett. 1969, 875.

Under these conditions rapid exchange of one of the two enantiotopic protons occurs; consequently, a "mono-tritio-glycine" was obtained. It is known, however, that treatment of D-alanine with amine oxidase affords 2-oxopropanoic acid (pyruvic acid), while L-alanine is not oxidized under the same conditions. Presuming that the stereoselectivity of the amine oxidase is the same in the case of glycine, it is thus the S proton which reacts in the oxidation of glycine to glyoxylic acid. Since oxidation of the "tritio-glycine" to glyoxylic acid with amine oxidase proceeds with retention of 83% of the tritium, it follows that the configuration is very probably $(R-1t)$.

4.2.3. Asymmetric Hydrolysis

The use of hydrolytic enzymes constitutes a useful method for the determination of configuration of acids and amino acids. In the case of amino acids, the success of the method depends on the greater susceptibility shown by the L-antipodes of an acetylated amino acid to the hydrolytic action of hog renal amidase or carboxy peptidase, or of the carboxamide to hog renal amidase. In practice, the racemic amino acid is either acetylated or converted into the carboxamide, and then subjected to the action of the enzyme; reaction occurs at 38° under neutral pH conditions. Only the derivative of the L-amino acid reacts with the enzyme, and the free amino acid thus formed can be separated from the non-hydrolyzed derivative of the D-amino acid.

$$R-CO-NH-\underset{R'}{\overset{COOH}{C}}-H \ , \ H-\underset{R'}{\overset{COOH}{C}}-NH-CO-R \ \xrightarrow{\text{carboxy peptidase or acylase I}} \ H_2N-\underset{R'}{\overset{COOH}{C}}-H \ + \ H-\underset{R'}{\overset{COOH}{C}}-NH-CO-R$$

$$H_2N-\underset{R'}{\overset{CO-NH_2}{C}}-H \ , \ H-\underset{R'}{\overset{CO-NH_2}{C}}-NH_2 \ \xrightarrow{\text{hog renal amidase}} \ H_2N-\underset{R'}{\overset{COOH}{C}}-H \ + \ H-\underset{R'}{\overset{CO-NH_2}{C}}-NH_2 \ + \ NH_3$$

The latter compound can be hydrolyzed by other methods to give the D-amino acid. The configurations of more than twenty amino acids have been elucidated in this way[81]. Still, with respect to amino acids, the protolytic enzymes function as catalysts both for the formation and hydrolysis of peptide linkages, i.e. for the equilibrium process:

$$\cdots-CO-NH-CH-CO-NH-CH-CO-NH-\cdots \ \underset{\underset{\text{protease}}{-H_2O}}{\overset{H_2O}{\rightleftharpoons}} \ \cdots-CO-NH-\underset{R^1}{CH}-COOH$$

$$+$$

$$H_2N-\underset{R^2}{CH}-CO-NH-\cdots$$

Formation of a peptide which is insoluble in the reaction medium shifts the equilibrium to the product side. This synthesis is stereoselective and L-directed, i.e. it is mainly the L-antipode of a racemate which participates in the condensation. Using these types of reactions it is possible to determine the configurations of several amino acids[82].
Studies on the stereospecificity of the action of leucine aminopeptidase on amino acids have revealed that the activity of the enzyme is restricted to derivatives of L-amino acids[83]. A number of L-leucyl-(±)-1-methylalkylamides has been subjected to the hydrolytic action of this enzyme[84]: in cases where the configuration of the amine was known, the L-leucyl(−)-1-methylalkylamide was

[81] P. Greenstein and M. Winitz, Chemistry of the Amino Acids, p. 148, John Wiley and Sons, 1961.
[82] P. Greenstein and M. Winitz, Chemistry of the Amino Acids, p. 150, John Wiley and Sons, 1961.
[83] E.L. Smith, D.H. Spackman, and J. Polglase, J. Biol. Chem. 199, 801 (1952).
[84] B. Halpern, J. Ricks, and J.W. Westley, Chem. Commun. 1966, 679.

preferentially hydrolyzed[84]. Hence, assuming similar enzyme stereospecificity, the absolute configuration L has been assigned to the amides of the (+)-methylalkylamines which were used.

The enzymatic stereospecificity of a-chymotrypsin has often been utilised, particularly in the hydrolyses of esters of carboxylic acids. The specificity of a-chymotrypsin has been claimed to be more relative than absolute[85]. Determination of the configuration of a given compound using a-chymotrypsin necessitates comparison of the results obtained in the enzymatic reactions with those available for the reactions of a series of compounds of similar structure under similar conditions. As in related comparative studies discussed earlier (see p. 97), the accuracy of this approach depends to a large extent on the number of examples used in the construction of the reference data. One example of the use of a-chymotrypsin is the determination of the configuration of 2-methoxycarbonyl-1-nitrosoindoline[86] (76) by comparison of the stereoselectivity of enzymatic hydrolysis of this substrate with those previously described (see p. 124) for the structurally related esters[87–89] 77, 78 and 79.

Chymotrypin-catalysed hydrolysis of (±)-76[86]

The racemic methyl ester 76 (0.08 g, 0.7 mmol) and a-chymotrypsin (0.08 g) in 0.1N sodium chloride (80 ml) are allowed to react under nitrogen using a "pH-stat" setting at pH 7.0, 0.1N sodium hydroxide being added from an automatic buret. After 30 hr, a base (1.862 ml) has been added, corresponding to 93% hydrolysis of one enantiomorph. The rate of reaction then becomes much slower. The reaction mixture is extracted with four 30 ml portions of ether. The extract (neutral fraction) is dried and evaporated to give a light yellow crystalline solid which is recrystallized to give a light yellow, neutral solid (34 mg) m.p.: 105–106°; $[a]_D^{27} = -26.5°$ (c = 0.40, ethanol), which on the basis of its infrared spectrum has been identified as the methyl ester 76 (laevo form).

The aqueous solution left after the extraction is acidified to pH 5 with 0.1N hydrochloric acid and extracted with four 25-ml portions of ether. The extract (acid fraction) is washed with water (10 ml) and treated with an ethereal solution of diazomethane till a faint yellow color persisted. Concentration under reduced pressure furnishes a light yellow crystalline solid which is recrystallized from ethyl acetate-pentane to give d-76 (30 mg) m.p.: 104°, $[a]_D^{27} = +43.95°$ (c = 0.48, ethanol).

The identity of the product is confirmed by comparison of the infrared spectrum with authentic methyl ester 76.

The Smolarsky method of amino acid synthesis involves as one stage an enzymatic resolution by means of a protease, chymotrypsin or subtilisine, viz.

The configurations of non-naturally occurring amino acid derivatives such as N-acetyl-3-(2-methylphenyl)-DL-alanine methyl ester and N-acetyl-3-(6-quinolinyl)-DL-alanine methyl ester have been determined in this way, i.e. via enzymic resolution[90].

In summary, enzymatic methods – especially as a consequence of the associated very high stereospecificities – are very valuable for the determination of configuration both of natural products and of non-naturally occurring molecules.

[85] H. Neurath and G.W. Schwert, Chem. Rev. 46, 69 (1950).

[86] E.J. Corey, R.J. McCaully, and H.S. Sachdev, J. Amer. Chem. Soc. 92, 2476 (1970).

[87] G. Hein, R.B. McGriff, and C. Niemann, J. Amer. Chem. Soc. 82, 1830 (1960).

[88] W.B. Lawson, J. Biol. Chem. 242, 3397 (1967).

[89] M.S. Silver and T. Sone, J. Amer Chem. Soc. 89, 457 (1967).

[90] A. Berger, M. Smolarsky, N. Kurn, and H.R. Bosshard, J. Org. Chem. 38, 457 (1973).

5. Conclusion

Many different methods of asymmetric synthesis and of resolution can be employed for the determination of configuration. The cautionary note sounded by Mislow[94] should, however, be noted:

"Conformational rules empirically derived from one type of system may not be legitimately extrapolated and transferred to another... This procedure is equally objectionable when the resulting configurational assignment proves to be correct..."

As a general rule, an asymmetric synthesis is founded on the basis of many examples in which the configuration of each compound is known, and assignments of configuration to compounds under study are then made by analogy. In cases where such an analogy cannot be or has not been established, it is essential to postulate a plausible topology for the diastereoisomeric transition states. Finally, it must be emphasized again that in the majority of cases it is imperative that strict adherence be paid to the experimental conditions associated with the derivation of an empirical correlation rule.

[91] J.P. Guetté, M. Perlat, J. Capillon, and D. Boucherot, Tetrahedron Lett. **28**, 2411 (1974).

[92] G. Vavon, C. Rivière and B. Angelo, C.R. Acad. Sci. Paris **222**, 959 (1946).

[93] J.P. Guetté and N. Spassky, Bull. Soc. Chim. France **1972**, 4217.

[94] K. Mislow, M.M. Green, P. Laur, J.T. Melillo, T. Simmons, and A.L. Ternay Jr., J. Amer. Chem. Soc. **87**, 1958 (1965).

Subject Index

Some abbreviations used:
absol. configur. = absolute configuration(s), asymmetr. = asymmetric, chem. = chemical, elucidat. = elucidation, enzymat. = enzymatic, relat. = relative, resolut. = resolution, retent. = retention, stereochem. = stereochemistry, subst. = substituted

Stereochemistry
Fundamentals and Methods

Edited by Prof. Henri B. Kagan
Laboratoire de Synthèse Asymétrique, Bâtiment 420
Université de Paris-Sud, Faculté des Sciences, Orsay/France

Also available:

Determination of Configurations by
Spectrometric Methods
(Vol. 1)

Contributions by
M. Golfier (IR Spectrometry), A. Gaudemer
(NMR Spectrometry), A. Mandelbaum (Mass
Spectrometry), R. Parthasarathy (X-Ray Analysis)
1977. VIII, 246 pages, 36 figures, 50 tables
17 x 24 cm, DM 88,—
ISBN 3 13 132501 1

Determination of Configurations by
Dipole Moments,
CD or ORD   (Vol. 2)

Contributions by
V. I. Minkin (Dipole Moments), M. Legrand and
M. J. Rougier (CD or ORD)
1977. VIII, 198 pages, 100 figures, 29 tables
17 x 24 cm, DM 72,—
ISBN 3 13 132601 8

Absolute Configurations
of 6000 Selected Compounds with
One Asymmetric
Carbon Atom   (Vol. 4)

By J. Jacques, C. Gros, and S. Bourcier
With the collaboration of M. J. Brienne and
J. Toullec
1977. XX, 602 pages, 17 x 24 cm
DM 158,—
ISBN 3 13 132801 0

In preparation:

Conformational Analysis
(Vol. 5)
Approx. 190 pages

Contributions by:
F. Riddell (Conformational Analysis), W. Hehre
and B. Devaquet (Conformational Analysis by
Perturbation or ab initio Molecular Orbital Theory)

Stereoisomerism and Thermo-
dynamics in Stereochemistry
(Vol. 6)
Approx. 155 pages

Contributions by:
M. Raban (Stereoisomerism), J. Reisse (Thermodynamic and Kinetic Basis of Stereochemistry)

Principles of Physical
Methods   (Vol. 7)
Approx. 160 pages

Contributions by:
V. I. Minkin (Dipole Moments), S. Mason (Cotton
Effect, CD or ORD), E. Kovats (Stereochemical
Aspects of Chromatography), R. Hakansson
(Quasi-Racemate Method)

Dynamic Stereochemistry
(Vol. 8)
Steric Course of Reactions, Synthesis of
Chiral Molecules
Approx. 210 pages

Contributions by:
J. Seyden-Penne (Steric Course of Reactions),
J. Gasteiger, D. Marquarding, and I. Ugi (The
Conceptual and Theoretical Foundations of
Chemical Chirality. Chiral Reactions and
Asymmetric Synthesis)

Principles of Spectrometric
Methods   (Vol. 9)
Approx. 250 pages

Contributions by:
A. Gaudemer and G. Martin (NMR Spectrometry),
M. Golfier (IR and Raman Spectrometry), Y. Mazur
and A. Yogev (UV, LD), B. Rees (X-Ray and
Neutron Diffraction), H. Kim (Microwave
Spectroscopy)

Further volumes on topical subjects are planned.

Georg Thieme Publishers Stuttgart